LOCATIONS
LOCATIONS
LOCATIONS

Ideal Settings
for Your Special Event
on the Monterey Peninsula

by Janice Block

ON THE COAST PUBLISHING

Published by On The Coast Publishing (An imprint of The Critic's Choice)
P.O. Box 223146
Carmel, CA 93922
(831) 624-3463
Copyright © 2002 by Janice Block

Cover Design: Elysium Design
Book Design: Linda Griffith
Cover Photos: ©Patrick Tregenza and ©Kevin Schafer/kevinschafer.com

Disclaimer
The author has made every reasonable effort to provide accurate and updated
information at the time *Locations, Locations, Locations* went to print. The author strongly
recommends that the reader call the facility to confirm that the data is accurate.
The author and publisher have tried to ensure accuracy; however, we assume no responsibility for any errors, omissions, or any other inconsistencies herein.

Photographers
Rudy Quidileg, Grant Huntington, Patrick Tregenza, Robert Miller, Russell Abraham,
Interface Visual, Robert Brown & Associates, Greg Wutke, Batista Moon Studio,
Patrice Ward, Craig Lovell, & Ed Young

Block, Janice
        Locations, Locations, Locations: Ideal Settings For Your Special
        Event On The Monterey Peninsula
        /Janice Block.-3rd ed. Includes Index

Library of Congress Catalog Card Number: 2002102638

ISBN 0-9632181-5-8 $15.95
        1. Weddings   2. Regional   3. Reference

Printed in the United States of America

ACKNOWLEDGMENTS

Thank you to all the participants for providing us with detailed information about your location. Without your help, this book would not have been possible.

Please Confirm...

We have made every reasonable effort to confirm the accuracy of all information in Locations, Locations, Locations. However, because prices, policies, and availability of locations and services are always subject to change, we strongly advise that you confirm prices and other specifications directly with the facility. You may either call the facility manager and ask them to confirm that information listed for their location is current,

OR

bring your copy of Locations, Locations, Locations to the facility when you visit and confirm the information at that time. Please keep in mind that the author and publisher assume no responsibility for errors, omissions, or any other inconsistencies in Locations, Locations, Locations.

Share Your Discoveries With Us!

Have you found a great new location for special events on the Monterey Peninsula? If so, let us know all about it so we can add it to our next edition of Locations, Locations, Locations. And if you discover any details we missed in this edition, let us know so we can update our information. The true test of any event location is whether you and your guests enjoy your experience at your selected location, so please take a moment to share your stories and suggestions. Send your comments to us at:

On The Coast Publishing

P.O. Box 223146

Carmel, CA 93922

(831) 624-3463

Fax (831) 685-8217

info@critics-choice.com

http://www.critics-choice.com

TABLE OF CONTENTS

INTRODUCTION

Locations, Locations,

Locations *is your ideal*

resource for planning a

wedding, corporate function,

or any other event on

California's Monterey

Peninsula. This book is

specially designed to save you

time while presenting you

with the many unique

event locations on the

exceptionally beautiful

Monterey Peninsula.

Planning an event can be a staggering task, especially if you are unfamiliar with the region you have chosen. We have done much of the legwork for you—making site visits, researching details, and using our in-depth knowledge of the Monterey Peninsula to bring you concise, well-organized information. Review this book before visiting the Peninsula, and you'll be fully prepared with a detailed listing of options and your own "short list" of locations to visit.

There are an overwhelming number of restaurants, hotels, and event sites on the Monterey Peninsula, so we have narrowed the choices down to make your search easier and faster. We handpicked these locations for their their time-tested quality, superb style and unparalleled attention to service. Our choices cover a variety of tastes, needs, and budgets to fit any event.

Whether you are organizing a wedding, corporate function, meeting, conference, receptions, reunion, office party, rehearsal dinner, bridal shower, luncheon, picnic, or other special event, this book is your best resource for information. Use it to compare your options quickly and effectively, and make a confident decision. With so many beautiful and unique sites on the Monterey Peninsula, this is your opportunity to select the perfect location for your event.

CATEGORY DESCRIPTIONS

The location descriptions use specific headings and phrases which may not be clear to you. This section explains what the terms mean.

AXIMUM CAPACITY

he maximum capacity for a given)om is broken down into two ategories: the maximum capacity for t-down meals, and the maximum :anding capacity for receptions where is assumed that most of the guests /ill not be seated. Some conference icilities may include theater seating apacities. Theater seating refers to a)om with rows of seats used for lec- ires.

YI: Capacities for buffet-style meals re not included, but a buffet usually ffers less seating than a sit-down 1eal.

1AIN DINING ROOM

he maximum seating capacity for the 1ain dining room will be listed : available.

RIVATE DINING ROOM

'rivate rooms are closed off from other liners.

EMIPRIVATE DINING ROOM

iemiprivate dining rooms are urrounded by three walls, so no other liners will walk through this area.

BANQUET ROOM

The maximum seating capacity is shown for the largest room in the facility. If other rooms are available with different capacities, information on those rooms will be included in the description. Also, full-service hotels can occasionally divide larger rooms into smaller rooms.

OUTDOOR FACILITY

If an outdoor area is available, the maximum seating capacity will be listed.

EXCLUSIVE USE OF INDOOR/ OUTDOOR FACILITIES

The facility may be rented for exclusive use. The minimum guest count required for exclusive use is listed.

AVAILABILITY OF FACILITIES

If a facility is not available year-round, the dates and times it is available will be included in the full description.

MEETING ROOMS

The number of meeting rooms available and the maximum seating capacity of the largest room will be listed for each location.

MEETING ROOM EQUIPMENT

If a facility offers meeting equipment, the types of equipment available will be described.

COCKTAIL PARTIES

The minimum cost per person will be listed for cocktail parties. This cost does not include food. Hors d'oeuvres are extra.

BANQUET/BUFFET MENU PRICES

Prices for banquet/buffet menus vary according to restaurant. The price ranges (food only) for lunch, dinner, and hors d'oeuvres are included.

ROOM RENTAL FEES

In some cases, the room rental fee depends on the number of guests. Room rates change, so call to verify prices with the facility.

DEPOSITS TO RESERVE A DATE

The deposit amounts required to reserve a date vary widely. Some facilities have a flat rate, while others charge a percentage of the estimated total billing.

FULL-SERVICE BAR

A full-service bar serves "hard" alcohol as well as wine, beer, and Champagne.

WINE AND BEER ONLY

Some locations serve only wine, beer, and Champagne.

CORKAGE FEE

If the site allows you to bring your own wine and champagne, there may be a fee to open your bottles.

DANCE FLOOR AREA

If there is space available for a dance floor, the description will state whether a dance floor is provided or whether one needs to be rented.

WHEELCHAIR ACCESS

Facilities accessible by wheelchair are noted.

SMOKING ALLOWED

If a location has an area for smokers, the description will list the site as outdoors.

LIVE MUSIC/ AMPLIFIED MUSIC

Live and/or amplified music is allowed, but there may be restrictions on where the music is allowed or how loud it may be. Please contact the facility manager for specific information on the area you are interested in.

EVENT COORDINATION SERVICES

An event coordinator will assist you in planning your event. The services offered vary according to the location and type of event.

WEDDING CEREMONY ON-SITE

Ceremony particulars will need to be discussed with the event coordinator or facility manager.

RESTAURANT SERVICES

There is an on-site restaurant that is available to your guests.

CATERING PROVIDED/ HIRE-YOUR-OWN (HYO) CATERER

This indicates whether catering is provided by the facility or whether you may hire your own caterer (HYO). If both options are available, both columns will be marked.

KITCHEN FACILITIES

There is an on-site kitchen available for your use.

WEDDING CAKES
BAKED IN-HOUSE
The facility can bake your wedding cake. Other options are also available.

OVERNIGHT
ACCOMMODATIONS
The number of available guest rooms is listed.

HOTEL DISCOUNT FOR
GUESTS OF EVENT
If the hotel offers a discount for guests of your event, you will need to call the facility to find out what discounts they offer.

COMPLIMENTARY
HOSPITALITY ROOM
The hotel provides a complimentary room for the bride and wedding party to prepare for the wedding.

Prices are subject to change. Please remember to confirm all prices with the facility.

RESTAURANTS WITH
PRIVATE DINING ROOMS

ANTON & MICHEL

*V*oted Restaurant of the Year in Carmel (recipient of the Green Ribbon of Excellence Award), Anton & Michel has been a landmark restaurant for over twenty years.

Considered the peninsula's most romantic restaurant, Anton & Michel offers cuisine, ambience, and service that are a hallmark blend of Old World elegance and modern charm. Rare oil paintings line the walls of the pastel-hued dining room, and floor-to-ceiling glass windows overlook the Court of the Fountains.

Creative continental cuisine is guided by Chef Max Mauramatsu, twice named Best Chef in Tokyo. Specialities include the highly acclaimed rack of lamb and chateaubriand, both carved tableside. Other entrées of distinction include fresh Monterey Bay seafood, fresh-farmed abalone, filet mignon, pistachio-crusted pork tenderloin, and loin of lamb. Attentive, professional service, an extensive award-winning wine list, full bar and specialty desserts all serve to reinforce the Wine Spectator's accolade that Anton & Michel is "probably the best dining experience in Carmel."

Court of the Fountains
Mission between Ocean and 7th
P.O. Box 4917
Carmel, CA 93921
(831) 624-2406
www.carmelsbest.com

CUISINE STYLE: *Creative Continental*

ROOMS AVAILABLE	MAXIMUM SEATING	MAXIMUM STANDING
Main Dining Room	100	150
Fireside Dining Room (private)	28	40
Outdoor Facilities	30	100
Exclusive Use of Indoor Facilities	120	150
Exclusive Use of Indoor and Outdoor Facilities	150	250

Exclusive Use of Outdoor Facilities: *Available with a minimum expenditure of $1,500 (excluding tax and tip)*

Exclusive Use of Indoor and Outdoor Facilities: *Available with a minimum expenditure of $7,500 (excluding tax and tip)*

Meeting Rooms: *None*

Availability of All Facilities: *Year-round*

Reserve for Events: *1 month in advance*

Reserve for Meetings: *n/a*

Cocktail Parties: *Allowed with a minimum expenditure of $15 per person (excluding tax and tip)*

Banquet Menu Prices Per Person (food only): *Luncheons $12.50-$27.50, Dinners $32.50-$47.50, Hors d'oeuvres $6.50-$17.50*

Buffet Menus: *n/a*

Room Rental Fee/Deposits: *There is no room rental fee. The deposit is 20% of the estimated total expenditure.*

Cancellation Policy: *Deposit is refundable with one week's notice*

Credit Cards: *AMX, Visa, M/C, Dis*

Parking: *Street*

Full-Service Bar: *Yes*

Corkage Fee: *$20*

Dance Floor: *No*

Wheelchair Accessible: *No*

Smoking Allowed: *No*

Live Music: *No*

Amplified Music: *No*

Event Coordination Services: *Yes*

Wedding Ceremony Allowed On-Site: *Yes*

Meeting Room Equipment: *None*

CASANOVA RESTAURANT

Nestled in amongst the Monterey Pines is Carmel-by-the-Sea's most romantic restaurant. Hand-painted tiles from Portugal and Italy line the pale-yellow and white plastered walls. The spectacular hand-dug thirty-thousand-bottle world-class wine cellar has received numerous awards. Dine outside on the gorgeous heated patio or inside in one of the uniquely European-style rooms.

An internationally renowned restaurant with Old World style, impeccable service and unrivaled charm, Casanova has four banquet rooms and an on-site event coordinator available. The Celebrity Room is just right for an intimate dinner. The Milagro Room, with its river-rock fireplace and antique angel chandeliers, is perfect for a small ceremony, reception, or both. The Harvest Room is a traditional French Provençal dining room with an open-hearth fireplace and wrought-iron chandeliers, a unique spot to hold that special event. The Havana Terrace, a lovely heated garden patio, may be used in conjunction with the other rooms.

Photo on Page P-2

5th Street between Mission and San Carlos
P.O. Box G.G.
Carmel, CA 93921
(831) 625-2727
www.casanovarestaurant.com

CUISINE STYLE: *Country French & Italian*

ROOMS AVAILABLE	MAXIMUM SEATING	MAXIMUM STANDING
Main Dining Room	100	n/a
Celebrity Room (private)	12	n/a
Milagro Room (private)	35	n/a
Harvest Room (private)	85	n/a
Outdoor Facilities	30	40

Exclusive Use of Entire Facility: *Yes*

Exclusive Use of Outdoor Facility: *Yes*

Meeting Rooms: *None*

Availability of All Facilities: *Year-round, except special-event weekends*

Reserve for Events: *1-6 months in advance*

Reserve for Meetings: *n/a*

Cocktail Parties: *No*

Banquet Menu Prices Per Person (food only): *Luncheons $22-$45, Dinners $65-$85, Hors d'oeuvres $7.50-$30*

Buffet Menu Prices Per Person (food only):
*Brunch from $25, Dinners n/a, Hors d'oeuvres
from $30*

Room Rental Fee/Deposits: *Minimum guar-
antees depending on date. The deposit is $375-
$500.*

Cancellation Policy: *Food and beverage
deposit is fully refundable with 30 days' prior
notice*

Credit Cards: *AMX, Visa, M/C*

Parking: *Street*

Full-Service Bar: *Yes*

Corkage Fee: *n/a*

Dance Floor: *Yes, area*

Wheelchair Accessible: *Yes*

Smoking Allowed: *Yes, outside*

Live Music: *Yes*

Amplified Music: *No*

Event Coordination Services: *Yes*

Wedding Ceremony Allowed On-Site: *Yes*

Meeting Room Equipment: *No*

FANDANGO

*E*njoy European country-style cuisine in a warm, Mediterranean setting. Crackling fires, baskets of freshly baked breads, flowers, and sunshine all add to Fandango's atmosphere. Choose from fresh seafood; regional dishes including pastas, paella, and couscous; or one of the specialties from the wood-burning grill. An international selection of premium wines, a full-service bar, and rich, decadent desserts complete this unique dining experience.

Fandango has a choice of private dining rooms, including a festive, ribbon-festooned wine cellar for smaller parties, as well as a semiprivate dining room and a glass-domed terrace. The wide array of room choices can accommodate groups ranging from sixteen to one hundred sixty guests.

Photo on Page P-3

223 17th Street
Pacific Grove, CA 93950
(831) 372-3456
www.fandangorestaurant.com

CUISINE STYLE: *European Grill*

ROOMS AVAILABLE	MAXIMUM SEATING	MAXIMUM STANDING
Main Dining Room	60	n/a
Banquet Room (private)	50	n/a
Banquet Room (private)	24	n/a
Cellar Room (private)	16	n/a
Dining Room (semiprivate)	40	n/a
Exclusive Use of Indoor Facilities	160	n/a
Banquet Room (private)	30	n/a

Exclusive Use of Indoor Facilities: *Available for a minimum expenditure of $10,000 to $15,000 (excluding tax and tip)*

Meeting Rooms: *None*

Availability of All Facilities: *Year-round*

Reserve for Events: *As soon as possible*

Reserve for Meetings: *As soon as possible*

Cocktail Parties: *Not allowed*

Banquet Menu Prices Per Person (food only): *Luncheons $20-$30, Dinners $29-$49, Hors d'oeuvres n/a*

Buffet Menu: *n/a*

Room Rental Fee/Deposits: *There is no room rental fee. Deposit is negotiable.*

Cancellation Policy: *30 days prior to event*

Credit Cards: *AMX, Visa, M/C, Dis*

Parking: *Lot, Street*

Full-Service Bar: *Yes*

Corkage Fee: *$20*

Dance Floor: *No*

Wheelchair Accessible: *Yes, except upstairs*

Smoking Allowed: *No*

Live Music: *Restricted*

Amplified Music: *No*

Event Coordination Services: *No*

Wedding Ceremony Allowed On-Site: *Yes*

Meeting Room Equipment: *Microphone*

FORGE IN THE FOREST

*T*he employee co-owners of The Forge in the Forest welcome you to this 10,000 square-foot historic Carmel landmark which has been voted "Best Outdoor Dining" every year since 1992! The Forge's award-winning garden patios are nestled among the oak and pine trees of downtown Carmel and are made comfortable year-round with fireplaces, heaters, and large patio umbrellas.

There are also four uniquely themed and appointed private dining areas. Whether you choose the Wine Cellar with its domed ceiling, wrought-iron chandelier and racks of large-format wine; the Gallery Showroom with the works of local artists; the Oak Tree Room, which has an entire wall that opens up and flows out to the garden setting of the Oak Tree Patio; or a complete property buyout, you will be bathed in Old World ambiance.

When you combine these very unique atmospheres with an executive chef who works with you one on one to custom tailor your menu, you are guaranteed an incredible dining experience that you and your guests will not soon forget.

Photo on Page P-4

S.W. Corner of 5th and Junipero
P.O. Box 6088
Carmel, CA 93921
(831) 624-RSVP
www.forgeintheforest.com

CUISINE STYLE: *American*

ROOMS AVAILABLE	MAXIMUM SEATING	MAXIMUM STANDING
Main Dining Room	40	50
The Wine Cellar (private)	16	20
The Oak Tree Room (private)	34	40
The Gallery (private)	45	50
Outdoor Facilities: Oak Tree Patio	32	50
Exclusive Use of Indoor and Outdoor Facilities	200	200

Exclusive Use of Entire Facility: *Yes, minimum expenditure is date dependent*

Meeting Rooms: *Yes*

Availability of All Facilities: *Year-round*

Reserve for Events: *Call for availability*

Reserve for Meetings: *Call for availability*

Cocktail Parties: *Yes*

Banquet and Buffet Menu Prices Per Person (food only): *Luncheons $12.95-$18.95, Dinners from $25, Hors d'oeuvres $1.25-$10*

Buffet Menu Prices Per Person (food only): *Luncheons $12.95-$18.95, Dinners from $25, Hors d'oeuvres $1.25-$10*

Room Rental Fee/Deposits: *The room rental fee is $150*

Cancellation Policy: *Deposit is refundable 30 days prior to event*

Credit Cards: *All major credit cards*

Parking: *Street, Lot, Valet can be arranged*

Full-Service Bar: *Yes*

Corkage Fee: *No, BYOB*

Dance Floor: *Yes*

Wheelchair Accessible: *Yes*

Smoking Allowed: *Outside*

Live Music: *No*

Amplified Music: *Yes, with restrictions*

Event Coordination Services: *Yes*

Wedding Ceremony Allowed On-Site: *Yes*

Meeting Room Equipment: *Yes*

FRESH CREAM

Stunning views of Monterey Harbor form the backdrop for several intimate dining rooms, while the main dining area boasts a clerestory skylight and comfortable banquet seating. All of this is set against interiors of light oak, muted grays, blues, and greens, lovely Impressionist art, and dramatic floral pieces. Fresh Cream is the recipient of two awards for interior design and another for architectural treatment.

Their nouvelle French cuisine with innovative California accents has won numerous awards and top ratings, including San Francisco Focus Magazine's readers' poll, the 1998 Dirona Award (Distinguished Restaurants of North America), and Conde Nast Traveler Magazine's Top 100 in America.

Photo on Page P-5

100C Heritage Harbor
Monterey, CA 93940
(831) 375-9798
www.freshcream.com

CUISINE STYLE: *French*

ROOMS AVAILABLE	MAXIMUM SEATING	MAXIMUM STANDING
Main Dining Room	65	100
Wine Room (private)	30	45
Executive Room (private)	48	70
Harbor Room (private)	20	n/a
Bay View Room (semiprivate)	24	n/a
Indoor Facilities	150	250
Outdoor Facilities	n/a	40

Exclusive Use of Indoor Facilities: *Available*

Exclusive Use of Outdoor Facilities: *n/a*

Exclusive Use of Entire Facility: *Available for a minimum expenditure of $7,500 to $20,000 (excluding tax and tip)*

Meeting Rooms: 3

Availability of All Facilities: *Year-round, after 5 p.m.*

Reserve for Events: *As soon as possible*

Reserve for Meetings: *As soon as possible*

Cocktail Parties: *Allowed*

Banquet Menu Prices Per Person (food only): *Luncheons from $3,000 min. on day use, Dinners from $45, Hors d' oeuvres from $5*

Buffet Menu: *n/a*

Room Rental Fee/Deposits: *Room rental fee varies from $250 to $500 depending on time and date. For groups of 16 or more the deposit is $30 per person.*

Cancellation Policy: *Deposit is refundable if notice is given 30 days prior to the event*

Credit Cards: *AMX, Visa, M/C, Dis*

Parking: *Parking Garage, Street*

Full-Service Bar: *Yes*

Corkage Fee: *$20*

Dance Floor: *No*

Wheelchair Accessible: *Yes*

Smoking Allowed: *On outside deck only*

Live Music: *Yes*

Amplified Music: *Yes*

Event Coordination Services: *Yes*

Wedding Ceremony Allowed On-Site: *Yes*

Meeting Room Equipment: *Available*

Il Fornaio

$\mathcal{I}$l Fornaio Cucina Italiana, situated in the heart of Carmel in the historic Pine Inn, serves authentic Italian cuisine. With a relaxed and intimate atmosphere, Il Fornaio is the perfect place for your wedding, reception, rehearsal dinner, or corporate function.

The Ocean Avenue Room, one of two private dining rooms, can accommodate up to seventy-five for a sit-down function and overlooks Ocean Avenue through a wall of windows, while French doors open onto the beautiful Piazza. The Piazza, with a view of Carmel Bay, accommodates seventy for a sit-down function and can be booked independently or in conjunction with the Ocean Avenue Room. The Rotunda can seat up to forty for a sit-down function. This circular room features a large brick fireplace and an opening glass ceiling.

Monte Verde at Ocean Avenue
Carmel, CA 93921
(831) 622-5108 Banquets
(831) 622-5100 Restaurant
www.ilfornaio.com

CUISINE STYLE: *Italian*

ROOMS AVAILABLE	MAXIMUM SEATING	MAXIMUM STANDING
Main Dining Room	160	200
Ocean Avenue Room	75	90
Rotunda	40	50
Outdoor Facilities	70	100
Exclusive Use of Indoor and Outdoor Facilities	145	190

Exclusive Use of Outdoor Facilities: *Available*

Exclusive Use of Indoor and Outdoor Facilities: *Available*

Exclusive Use of Entire Facility: *Available*

Meeting Rooms: 2

Availability of All Facilities: *Year-round*

Reserve for Events: *1 year*

Reserve for Meetings: *1 year*

Cocktail Parties: *Allowed with a minimum expenditure of $20 per person (excluding tax and tip)*

Banquet and Buffet Menu Prices Per Person (food only): *Luncheons from $19.95-$25.95, Dinners from $34.95-52.95, Hors d'oeuvres from $35 for plates*

Room Rental Fee/Deposits: *There are modest minimums on the private dining rooms in lieu of a room rental charge. Reserve room with credit card guarantee.*

Cancellation Policy: *Cancellation policy is negotiable*

Credit Cards: *AMX, Visa, M/C, Dis*

Parking: *Street*

Full-Service Bar: *Yes*

Corkage Fee: *n/a*

Dance Floor: *Can be arranged*

Wheelchair Accessible: *Yes*

Smoking Allowed: *Yes, Piazza only*

Live Music: *Yes, inside*

Amplified Music: *No*

Event Coordination Services: *Yes*

Wedding Ceremony Allowed On-Site: *Yes*

Meeting Room Equipment: *Can be arranged*

MONTRIO

*T*ake the influences of the best European-American cuisine, add a delightfully updated Monterey firehouse, combine the two with great service and you have Montrio. This bistro with big-city ambience features a comfortable well-stocked bar and award-winning wine list. Montrio also features two private rooms that are ideal for celebrations or business functions and a full-service banquet department. Montrio's dedication to fresh ingredients is expressed in its flavorful dishes such as Grilled Gulf Prawns over Caramelized-Leek Risotto, Oven-Roasted Portabella Mushroom over Crispy Polenta, and Chocolate Brioche Bread Pudding. The insistence that dining should be casual and fun has made Montrio Monterey's favorite restaurant for all occasions.

Photo on Page P-13

414 Calle Principal
Monterey, CA 93940
(831) 648-8881 (Banquets)
www.montrio.com

CUISINE STYLE: *American Bistro*

ROOMS AVAILABLE	MAXIMUM SEATING	MAXIMUM STANDING
Main Dining Room	120	300
Jazz Room (private)	24	50
Parker Room (private)	80	150
Exclusive Use of Indoor Facilities	240	500

Exclusive Use of Entire Facility: *Available with a minimum expenditure*

Meeting Rooms: *2 meeting rooms are available that can seat from 10 to 70 guests*

Availability of All Facilities: *Year-round*

Reserve for Events: *As much notice as possible*

Reserve for Meetings: *As much notice as possible*

Cocktail Parties: *Yes*

Banquet Menu Prices Per Person (food only): *Luncheons $11-$26, Dinners $24-$60, Hors d'oeuvres $1.50-$5.75*

Buffet Menu: Per Person (food only): *Luncheons $10-$40, Dinners $20-$60, Hors d'oeuvres $1.50-$5.75*

Room Rental Fee/Deposits: *Room rental fees vary from $25 to $300*

Cancellation Policy: *Deposit is refundable with 30 days' written cancellation notice*

Credit Cards: *AMX, Visa, M/C, Dis*

Parking: *Lot, Street*

Full-Service Bar: *Yes*

Corkage Fee: *$12*

Dance Floor: *Can be arranged*

Wheelchair Accessible: *Yes (Main Dining Room)*

Smoking Allowed: *No*

Live Music: *Yes*

Amplified Music: *Yes*

Event Coordination Services: *Yes*

Wedding Ceremony Allowed On-Site: *Yes*

Meeting Room Equipment: *Yes*

Old Bath House Restaurant

This Victorian-era restaurant features an extraordinary setting, right over the Pacific Ocean at romantic Lovers Point Park. With a panoramic view of the Monterey Bay by day and night, this location is truly one of a kind.

Equally breathtaking are the impeccable service and cuisine at this landmark location. Winner of local, national, and international acclaim, the staff at the Old Bath House shows attention to every minute detail. The menu offers a broad selection of updated classics—Rack of Lamb Encrusted with Pistachios, Venison Tenderloin with Pearl Onions and Pomegranate Reduction, Alaskan Halibut Encrusted with Cracked Black Pepper, and Coriander over Lemon Risotto highlight just a few of the varied entrée offerings. If you have room left to sample only one dessert, try either the Grand Marnier or Chocolate Soufflé. There is also an outstanding wine list and full-bar service to complement the menu.

620 Ocean View Boulevard
Pacific Grove, CA 93950
(831) 375-5195
www.oldbathhouse.com

CUISINE STYLE: *New Traditional*

ROOMS AVAILABLE	MAXIMUM SEATING	MAXIMUM STANDING
Main Dining Room	75	90
Exclusive Use of Indoor Facility	75	90

Exclusive Use of Indoor Facility: *Available for a minimum expenditure of $80 per person (excluding tax and tip)*

Meeting Rooms: *No*

Availability of All Facilities: *Year-round*

Reserve for Events: *1 month in advance*

Reserve for Meetings: *n/a*

Cocktail Parties: *Not allowed*

Banquet Menu Prices Per Person (food only): *Luncheons from $24.95, Dinners from $39.50, Hors d'oeuvres n/a*

Buffet Menu: *Available for brunch or lunch*

Room Rental Fee/Deposits: *The room rental fee is $500. The deposit to reserve a date is 30% of the estimated total expenditure.*

Cancellation Policy: *50% of deposit is refundable with 7 days' notice*

Credit Cards: *AMX, Visa, M/C, Dis, Diners*

Parking: *Lot nearby, Street*

Full-Service Bar: *Yes*

Corkage Fee: *$20*

Dance Floor: *Yes, with groups of 45 or less*

Wheelchair Accessible: *No*

Smoking Allowed: *No*

Live Music: *No*

Amplified Music: *Yes*

Event Coordination Services: *Yes*

Wedding Ceremony Allowed On-Site: *Yes*

Meeting Room Equipment: *None*

PASSIONFISH

assionfish, located in charming downtown Pacific Grove, features line-caught local fish, slow-cooked meats, and beautiful greens from down the road. With a passion for cooking and an appreciation for seasonal ingredients, Ted Walter, owner and chef, offers simple, inspired meals emphasizing quality ingredients at their peak of freshness. Determined to prepare his dishes with the finest foods, the chef continually shops the farmer's market and seeks out local organic farmers.

Combining the rich flavors of his finds, the menu at Passionfish reminds us that the source of food's pleasure is its flavor. The meals are complemented by many rare and desirable international wines at amazingly affordable prices and a unique beer list ranging from African to Belgian selections. Regardless of your group's size, the staff at Passionfish offers easy, flexible menu planning to help customize your special event.

Photo on Page P-14

701 Lighthouse Avenue
Pacific Grove, CA 93950
(831) 655-3311
www.passionfish.net

CUISINE STYLE: *California*

ROOMS AVAILABLE	MAXIMUM SEATING	MAXIMUM STANDING
Main Dining Room	125	250
Private Dining Room	32	43
Semiprivate Dining Room	60	n/a
Outdoor Facilities	14	18
Exclusive Use of Indoor Facilities	125	250

Exclusive Use of Indoor Facilities: *Available for a minimum expenditure of $8,000 (excluding tax and tip)*

Meeting Rooms: 2

Availability of All Facilities: *Year-round*

Reserve for Events: *2 weeks in advance*

Reserve for Meetings: *As soon as possible*

Cocktail Parties: *n/a*

Banquet Menu Prices Per Person (food only): *Luncheons from $15, Dinners from $26, Hors d'oeuvres from $10*

Buffet Menu: *n/a*

Room Rental Fee/Deposits: *There is no room rental fee. The deposit is 25% of the estimated total expenditure.*

Cancellation Policy: *Deposit is refundable if cancellation is made 72 hours prior to event*

Credit Cards: *AMX, Visa, M/C, Dis*

Parking: *Street*

Full-Service Bar: *No, wine and beer only*

Corkage Fee: *$10*

Dance Floor: *No*

Wheelchair Accessible: *Yes*

Smoking Allowed: *No*

Live Music: *No*

Amplified Music: *Yes*

Event Coordination Services: *Yes*

Wedding Ceremony Allowed On-Site: *No*

Meeting Room Equipment: *None*

Rio Grill

io Grill captures the soul of the Southwest with attractive Southwestern decor. Colorful and exciting art, cacti, and succulents are a big part of the contemporary atmosphere along with butcher paper–covered tables for the young at heart. Creative American food is well represented at Rio Grill, where the freshest ingredients and an oakwood smoker give the appetizers and entrées a wonderful flair. The menu features an array of salads and sandwiches with a number of entrées, including daily fresh fish, pastas, rabbit, duck, and wonderful vegetarian choices. Rio Grill boasts an award-winning wine list featuring over two hundred California labels as well as a large selection served by the glass. Consistently named "Best Restaurant in Monterey County," the restaurant has now added "Best American Restaurant" and "Best Place to Meet People" to its list of accolades. The friendly staff will be happy to help you plan the perfect event.

Photo on Page P-16

The Crossroads
Highway 1 at Rio Road
Carmel, CA 93923
(831) 625-5437
www.riogrill.com

CUISINE STYLE: *Creative American Grill*

ROOMS AVAILABLE	MAXIMUM SEATING	MAXIMUM STANDING
Main Dining Room	170	250
Santa Fe Room	50	75
Semiprivate Dining Room	34	40
Outdoor Facilities	40	80

Exclusive Use of Outdoor Facilities: *Available with a minimum expenditure*

Exclusive Use of Entire Facility: *Available with a minimum expenditure*

Meeting Rooms: *2 meeting rooms that seat 40 and 60 guests*

Availability of All Facilities: *Year-round*

Reserve for Events: *Please call for reservations*

Reserve for Meetings: *Please call for reservations*

Cocktail Parties: *Yes*

Banquet Menu Prices Per Person (food only): *Luncheons $10-$18, Dinners $22-$45, Hors d'oeuvres $6-$14*

Buffet Menu: *n/a*

Room Rental Fee/Deposits: *The room rental fee varies from $25-$150. The deposit to reserve a date is $100.*

Cancellation Policy: *Deposit is refundable with 30 days' cancellation notice*

Credit Cards: *AMX, Visa, M/C, Dis*

Parking: *Lot*

Full-Service Bar: *Yes*

Corkage Fee: *$12*

Dance Floor: *No*

Wheelchair Accessible: *Yes*

Smoking Allowed: *No*

Live Music: *No*

Amplified Music: *Yes*

Event Coordination Services: *Yes*

Wedding Ceremony Allowed On-Site: *Yes*

Meeting Room Equipment: *Yes*

THE SARDINE FACTORY RESTAURANT

The Sardine Factory Restaurant, world famous as "The Flagship of Cannery Row," serves award-winning cuisine featuring local seafood, prime steaks, and chops. Intimate dinners and group functions for up to one hundred are individually served by a highly trained staff.

The six distinctively appointed dining rooms may be viewed on the Internet at www.sardinefactory.com. Weddings and receptions are a specialty at the Factory, whose hallmark is individual planning for each event.

Photo on Page P-17

701 Wave Street
Monterey, CA 93940
(831) 373-3775
www.sardinefactory.com

CUISINE STYLE: *Seafood*

ROOMS AVAILABLE	MAXIMUM SEATING	MAXIMUM STANDING
Cannery Row Room	75	n/a
Captain's Room	50	n/a
The Conservatory	100	n/a
Wine Cellar	28	n/a
Original Wine Cellar	12	n/a
Steinbeck Room	16	n/a
Exclusive Use of Indoor Facilities	225	300

Exclusive Use of Indoor Facilities: *Available*

Meeting Rooms: *3 meeting rooms*

Availability of All Facilities: *Year-round*

Reserve for Events: *As soon as possible*

Reserve for Meetings: *As soon as possible*

Cocktail Parties: *n/a*

Banquet Menu Prices Per Person (food only): *Specially created luncheon and dinner menus*

Buffet Menu Prices Per Person (food only): *n/a*

Room Rental Fee/Deposits: *Yes*

Cancellation Policy: *Yes*

Credit Cards: *AMX, Visa, M/C, Dis*

Parking: *Complimentary*

Full-Service Bar: *Yes*

Corkage Fee: *Yes*

Dance Floor: *No*

Wheelchair Accessible: *Yes*

Smoking Allowed: *No*

Live Music: *No*

Amplified Music: *Yes*

Event Coordination Services: *Yes*

Wedding Ceremony Allowed On-Site: *No*

Meeting Room Equipment: *Yes*

STOKES RESTAURANT & BAR

The spectacular Stokes Restaurant & Bar is located in the heart of downtown Monterey in a beautiful 1833 two-story adobe. For over one hundred fifty years, this building has been at the center of Monterey's social life, beginning with the Cascaron balls that mayor James Stokes held in its sala in the mid-1800s. Now, Stokes offers guests fabulous food in an incomparable setting that provides beauty as well as versatility: six separate dining areas of varying sizes boast thick adobe walls, hardwood and Spanish-tiled floors, multi-paned windows, fireplaces, balconies, and distressed Renaissance-style ornamental painting. Every room, large or small, retains the warmth and charm of the home that the Stokes building once was.

Stokes features the award-winning Mediterranean cuisine of San Francisco chef Brandon Miller. Complement your meal with the fabulous wine list, full bar, and friendly professional service.

Photo on Page P-18

500 Hartnell Street
Monterey, CA 93940
(831) 373-1110
www.stokesadobe.com

CUISINE STYLE: *California Mediterranean*

ROOMS AVAILABLE	MAXIMUM SEATING	MAXIMUM STANDING
Main Dining Room	75	125
Captain's Room (private)	12	n/a
Wine Room (private)	46	50
Hattie's Room (private)	30	40
The Lounge	24	40
Exclusive Use of Indoor Facilities	200	250

Exclusive Use of Indoor Facilities: *Available for a minimum expenditure of $18,000 (excluding tax and tip), with a minimum guest count of 75*

Meeting Rooms: *3*

Availability of All Facilities: *Year-round*

Reserve for Events: *1 month in advance to 1 year*

Reserve for Meetings: *1 month in advance to 1 year*

Cocktail Parties: *Allowed with a minimum expenditure of $18 per person (excluding tax and tip)*

Banquet Menu Prices Per Person (food only): *Luncheons $17-30, Dinners $35-$75, Hors d'oeuvres $17-$40*

Buffet Menu: *n/a*

Room Rental Fee/Deposits: *$50-$500/$250 deposit*

Cancellation Policy: *Please call*

Credit Cards: *AMX, Visa, M/C, Diners*

Parking: *Lot, Street*

Full-Service Bar: *Yes*

Corkage Fee: *$15*

Dance Floor: *No*

Wheelchair Accessible: *Yes*

Smoking Allowed: *No*

Live Music: *Yes*

Amplified Music: *Yes*

Event Coordination Services: *Yes*

Wedding Ceremony Allowed On-Site: *Yes*

Meeting Room Equipment: *Yes*

Tarpy's Roadhouse

*E*njoy the country charm of Tarpy's Roadhouse, sister restaurant of the famous Rio Grill of Carmel. Set in Hacienda Saucito, the original Ryan Ranch family homestead that dates back to 1917, Tarpy's Roadhouse successfully mixes local history, fabulous Creative American Country cuisine and warm personal service. The rambling stone structure in the rolling hills of Monterey has been an oasis since the 1940s, when it housed the popular Cademartori's. Today, the extensive gardens, European-style courtyards, and cozy, fire-lit interiors have made it a popular destination for locals and visitors alike. The restaurant features updated versions of old-fashioned "comfort" foods using only the freshest ingredients. Whether you enjoy a sunny luncheon on the patio or a festive party in one of the many private dining rooms, the great food, beautiful atmosphere, and friendly, professional service combine to make dining at Tarpy's Roadhouse an event to be remembered.

Photo on Page P-19

2999 Monterey/Salinas Highway
Monterey, CA 93940
(831) 647-1444 (Main Dining Room)
www.tarpys.com

CUISINE STYLE: *Creative American Country*

ROOMS AVAILABLE	MAXIMUM SEATING	MAXIMUM STANDING
Main Dining Room	165	300
Library (private)	80	120
Vintner's Room (private)	36	50
Sarah's Room (semiprivate)	36	50
Tack Room (private)	16	25
Shell Room (semiprivate)	26	n/a
Outdoor Facilities	80	200
Exclusive Use of Indoor and Outdoor Facilities	300	500

Exclusive Use of Outdoor Facilities: *Available for a minimum expenditure*

Exclusive Use of Entire Facility: *Available for a minimum expenditure*

Meeting Rooms: *6 meeting rooms that seat from 6 to 80 guests*

Availability of All Facilities: *Year-round*

Reserve for Events: *As much notice as possible*

Reserve for Meetings: *As much notice as possible*

Cocktail Parties: *Yes*

Banquet Menu Prices Per Person (food only): *Luncheons $12-$30, Dinners $22-$50, Hors d'oeuvres $10-$40*

Buffet Menu Prices Per Person (food only): *Luncheons $10-$40, Dinners $22-$50, Hors d'oeuvres $6-$30*

Room Rental Fee/Deposits: *Room rental fees vary from $25 to $150. Deposit is $100.*

Cancellation Policy: *Deposit is refundable with 30 days' cancellation notice*

Credit Cards: *AMX, Visa, M/C, Dis*

Parking: *Lot*

Full-Service Bar: *Yes*

Corkage Fee: *$12*

Dance Floor: *Yes, area*

Wheelchair Accessible: *Yes*

Smoking Allowed: *Restricted to outdoors only*

Live Music: *Yes*

Amplified Music: *Yes*

Event Coordination Services: *Yes*

Wedding Ceremony Allowed On-Site: *Yes*

Meeting Room Equipment: *Yes*

THE TINNERY

The Tinnery boasts unparalleled views of the Monterey Bay from Lovers Point in Pacific Grove. Dining is relaxed and affordable whether your party is in the main dining room, the Cove Room, or the solarium. The diverse menu ranges from seafood and filet mignon to pizzas and burgers to traditional favorites like turkey and smoked ham.

The restaurant can accommodate anything from large parties in their banquet facilities to intimate cocktail parties in their lounge. The Tinnery will also coordinate outdoor weddings at Lovers Point Park directly in front of the restaurant. This memorable setting is a dramatic backdrop for any event.

631 Ocean View Boulevard
Pacific Grove, CA 93950
(831) 646-1040
www.thetinnery.com

CUISINE STYLE: *American*

ROOMS AVAILABLE	MAXIMUM SEATING	MAXIMUM STANDING
Main Dining Room	140	n/a
Banquet Room	110	n/a
Private Dining Room	50	n/a
Cove Room (semiprivate)	35	n/a
Outdoor Facilities	50	60

Exclusive Use of Indoor Facilities: *n/a*

Exclusive Use of Outdoor Facilities: *Available for a negotiable minimum expenditure*

Meeting Rooms: *2 meeting rooms that can seat 35 and 50 guests*

Availability of All Facilities: *Year-round*

Reserve for Events: *1 week in advance*

Reserve for Meetings: *1 week in advance*

Cocktail Parties: *Allowed with a minimum expenditure of $8 per person (excluding tax and tip)*

Banquet Menu Prices Per Person (food only): *Luncheons $12-$15, Dinners $17-$28, Hors d'oeuvres $4-$7*

Buffet Menu: *n/a*

Room Rental Fee/Deposits: *There is no room rental fee with meal functions. With cocktail parties and meetings, the fee is negotiable. The deposit to reserve a room is $150.*

Cancellation Policy: *Deposit is nonrefundable*

Credit Cards: *AMX, Visa, M/C, Dis, Diners*

Parking: *Lot, Street*

Full-Service Bar: *Yes*

Corkage Fee: *$10*

Dance Floor: *No*

Wheelchair Accessible: *Yes*

Smoking Allowed: *No*

Live Music: *No*

Amplified Music: *No*

Event Coordination Services: *Yes*

Wedding Ceremony Allowed On-Site: *Yes*

Meeting Room Equipment: *Yes*

VITO'S

*A*t Vito's, voted "Best Italian Restaurant," Vito and his family prepare their recipes with an Old World flair in a casual and friendly atmosphere. Relax and choose from a menu that includes an extensive array of antipasti, fresh fish, chicken, veal, pasta entrées and an irresistible dessert menu (including tiramisu made from the family's secret recipe). In true Sicilian fashion, no one walks away hungry.

32 Forest Avenue
Pacific Grove, CA 93950
(831) 375-3070

CUISINE STYLE: *Italian*

ROOMS AVAILABLE	MAXIMUM SEATING	MAXIMUM STANDING
Main Dining Room	75	n/a
Private Dining Room	40	n/a

Exclusive Use of Entire Facility: *Yes*

Meeting Rooms: *n/a*

Availability of All Facilities: *Year-round*

Reserve for Events: *As soon as possible*

Reserve for Meetings: *n/a*

Cocktail Parties: *No*

Banquet Menu Prices Per Person (food only): *Dinners from $25, Hors d'oeuvres n/a*

Buffet Menu: *n/a*

Room Rental Fee/Deposits: *There is no room rental fee. The deposit is $300.*

Cancellation Policy: *The deposit is nonrefundable*

Credit Cards: *AMX, Visa, M/C, Dis, Diners*

Parking: *Lot, Street*

Full-Service Bar: *No, wine and beer only*

Corkage Fee: *$10*

Dance Floor: *No*

Wheelchair Accessible: *Yes*

Smoking Allowed: *No*

Live Music: *No*

Amplified Music: *Yes*

Event Coordination Services: *No*

Wedding Ceremony Allowed On-Site: *Yes*

Meeting Room Equipment: *None*

Hotels, Bed & Breakfasts, Resorts, Inns, and Conference Facilities

ASILOMAR CONFERENCE GROUNDS

Since its founding in 1913, the Asilomar Conference Grounds has provided visitors with the retreat atmosphere that is very conducive to successful meetings, and the exquisite natural environment and historic architecture that create the perfect setting for a romantic wedding, an anniversary banquet, a reunion, or any other celebration. The wide variety of spaces situated throughout the campus layout in a natural park setting make Asilomar an ideal location for almost any group.

Asilomar offers dining options that include custom-planned menus and other services that your meeting or event requires, including audio-visual, floral, and entertainment services through local providers.

Altogether, Asilomar has approximately 27,000 square feet of space available. There are twenty meeting rooms and twenty break-out rooms, ranging in size from the six-hundred-fifty seat Merrill Hall and two-hundred seat Chapel to the smaller, intimate living rooms, several with fireplaces, accommodating ten individuals.

800 Asilomar Avenue
Pacific Grove, CA 93950
(831) 642-4222
www.visitasilomar.com

ROOMS AVAILABLE	MAXIMUM SEATING	MAXIMUM STANDING	MAXIMUM THEATER
Multiple Room	250	450	n/a
Outdoor Facilities: Meadow BBQ Area	1,200	1,500	n/a

Exclusive Use of Indoor Facilities: *Available*

Exclusive Use of Outdoor Facilities: *Available*

Meeting Rooms: *38 meeting rooms*

Availability of All Facilities: *Year-round*

Reserve for Events: *Up to 1 year in advance*

Reserve for Meetings: *Up to 2 years in advance*

Cocktail Parties: *Allowed with a catering order*

Banquet Menu Prices Per Person (food only): *Luncheons $14-$25, Dinners $20-$50, Hors d'oeuvres $12-$50*

Buffet Menu Prices Per Person (food only): *Luncheons $16-$30, Dinners from $24, Hors d'oeuvres from $12*

Room Rental Fee/Deposits: *The room rental fee is $150 and up. The deposit for events is nonrefundable*

Cancellation Policy: *Deposit is refundable without penalty with 60 days' notice*

Credit Cards: *AMX, Visa, M/C*

Parking: *Lot, Street*

Full-Service Bar: *No*

Corkage Fee: *n/a*

Dance Area: *Yes*

Dance Floor: *Yes*

Wheelchair Accessible: *Yes*

Smoking Allowed: *No*

Live Music: *Yes*

Amplified Music: *Yes*

Event Coordination Services: *Yes*

Wedding Ceremony Allowed On-Site: *Yes*

Meeting Room Equipment: *Yes*

Sound System: *Available in some rooms*

Elevated Stage: *Yes*

Audio Visual: *Yes*

Restaurant Services: *No*

Catering Provided: *Yes*

HYO Caterer: *No*

Kitchen Facilities: *No*

Linens, Silver, Glasses, etc. Provided: *Yes*

Tables and Chairs Provided: *Yes*

Wedding Cakes Baked In-House: *No*

In-House Florist: *No*

Overnight Accommodations: *313 guest rooms*

Hotel Discount for Guests of Event: *No*

Complimentary Hospitality Rooms: *No*

THE BEACH RESORT

A sweep of pale sand set beneath the miles of dunes, the high keening of seagulls, sunsets where the dolphins and whales play, and the roar of the waves as the Pacific Ocean tumbles to shore form an idyllic setting.

Life is for living at the most beautiful bay on the coast of California. The Beach Resort is a spot where memories of life's greater moments are created. A world-class experience to delight business and leisure travelers.

Monterey's only beach-front resort directly on the beach, one hundred ninety-six ocean-view and garden rooms with voice mail and dataport phones, concierge service, in-room dining, fitness center, heated pool, spa, business center, ocean-view and executive conference rooms.

Gourmet restaurant, lounge, and espresso bar. Enjoy the sunset with your favorite beverage and live entertainment. An ideal setting for romantic getaways, weddings, meetings, and corporate functions. An experience to remember!

Photo on Page P-1

2600 Sand Dunes Drive
Monterey, CA 93940
(800) 242-8627 (Reservations)
(831) 394-3321 (Resort)
www.montereybeachresort.com

ROOMS AVAILABLE	MAXIMUM SEATING	MAXIMUM STANDING	MAXIMUM THEATER
Cafe Beach	125	250	n/a
La Grande Room	175	310	290
Points Ballroom	390	550	520
Captain's Table	40	75	80
Bayview Room	100	88	100
Outdoor Facilities:			
South Garden	75	100	75

Exclusive Use of Outdoor Facilities: *Available*

Meeting Rooms: *10 meeting rooms with various capacities*

Availability of All Facilities: *Year-round*

Reserve for Events: *As soon as possible*

Reserve for Meetings: *As soon as possible*

Cocktail Parties: *Allowed with a minimum expenditure of $20 per person (excluding tax and tip)*

Banquet Menu Prices Per Person (food only): *Luncheons from $15, Dinners from $22, Hors d'oeuvres from $20*

Buffet Menu Prices Per Person (food only): *Luncheons from $19, Dinners from $29, Hors d'oeuvres from $20*

Room Rental Fee/Deposits: *The room rental fee varies. The deposit to reserve a date is $1,000.*

Cancellation Policy: *Deposit refund varies. Cancellation policy varies.*

Credit Cards: *AMX, Visa, M/C, Dis, Diners*

Parking: *Lot*

Full-Service Bar: *Yes*

Corkage Fee: *$10*

Dance Floor: *Yes*

Wheelchair Accessible: *Yes*

Smoking Allowed: *No*

Live Music: *Yes*

Amplified Music: *Yes*

Event Coordination Services: *Yes*

Wedding Ceremony Allowed On-Site: *Yes*

Meeting Room Equipment: *Available upon request*

Sound System: *Yes*

Elevated Stage: *Yes*

Audio Visual: *Yes*

Restaurant Services: *Yes*

Catering Provided: *Yes*

HYO Caterer: *No*

Kitchen Facilities: *Hotel use only*

Linens, Silver, Glasses, etc. Provided: *Yes*

Tables and Chairs Provided: *Yes*

Wedding Cakes Baked In-House: *No*

In-House Florist: *No*

Overnight Accommodations: *196 guest rooms*

Hotel Discount for Guests of Event: *Negotiable*

Complimentary Hospitality Rooms: *No*

BERNARDUS LODGE

*N*estled on verdant acres with stands of stately pines, surrounded by a vineyard and the Santa Lucia mountains rising majestically in the background, Bernardus Lodge is a premier luxury resort that combines the simple elegance of fine country living with the high-quality service and luxury amenities found in only the choicest European hotels.

The resort features fifty-seven sumptuous suites located in nine single- and two-story adobe village-style buildings along a terraced hillside. The resort also features a luxurious spa, ballroom and function space, swimming pool, two tennis courts, a croquet lawn, wedding pavilion, and vineyard.

Bernardus Lodge can accommodate meetings and special events with more than 4,200 square feet of flexible meeting and function space. A specially designed wedding pavilion can accommodate up to one hundred fifty guests in an elegant and romantic setting. An additional 5,000 square feet of beautifully landscaped outdoor function space is also available.

415 Carmel Valley Road
Carmel Valley, CA 93924
(831) 658-3400
www.bernardus.com

ROOMS AVAILABLE	MAXIMUM SEATING	MAXIMUM STANDING	MAXIMUM THEATER
Wedding Pavilion	150	150	150
Meritage Ballroom	150	180	180
Harvest Room	50	60	60
Magnum Boardroom	14	14	n/a
2-Bedroom Conference Suite	12	25	n/a

Exclusive Use of Outdoor Facility: *Yes*

Meeting Rooms: *4 meeting rooms that seat up to 180 guests*

Availability of All Facilities: *Year-round*

Reserve for Events: *Up to 1 year in advance*

Reserve for Meetings: *As soon as possible*

Cocktail Parties: *Allowed with a minimum expenditure of $25 per person (excluding tax and gratuity)*

Banquet Menu Prices Per Person (food only): *Luncheons $30-$45, Dinners $55-$85, Hors d'oeuvre prices vary*

Buffet Menu Per Person (food only): *Luncheons $30-$45, Dinners $55-$85*

Room Rental Fee/Deposits: *Room rental fee is $2,500 for the Ballroom and $1,000 for the Pavilion. The deposit is the room rental fee.*

Cancellation Policy: *Call for details*

Credit Cards: *AMX, Visa, M/C, Dis, Diners, JCB*

Parking: *Lot, Complimentary Valet*

Full-Service Bar: *Yes*

Corkage Fee: *$20*

Dance Floor: *Yes*

Wheelchair Accessible: *Yes*

Smoking Allowed: *No*

Live Music: *Yes, with restrictions*

Amplified Music: *Indoors only*

Event Coordination Services: *Yes*

Wedding Ceremony Allowed On-Site: *Yes*

Meeting Room Equipment: *Upon request*

Sound System: *Yes*

Elevated Stage: *Yes*

Audio Visual: *Yes*

Restaurant Services: *Yes*

Catering Provided: *Yes*

HYO Caterer: *No*

Kitchen Facilities: *Yes*

Linens, Silver, Glasses, etc. Provided: *Yes*

Tables and Chairs Provided: *Yes*

Wedding Cakes Baked In-House: *Yes*

In-House Florist: *No*

Overnight Accommodations: *57 guest rooms*

Hotel Discount for Guests of Event: *Yes, on a limited basis*

Complimentary Hospitality Rooms: *No*

CARMEL MISSION INN

The Carmel Mission Inn combines the feel of a charming country inn with one hundred sixty-five newly decorated, elegant guest rooms and offers a lovely garden setting, swimming pool, spas, restaurant, lounge, and meeting facilities that accommodate up to three hundred. The hotel is adjacent to one hundred seventy-five boutiques, restaurants, shops, and galleries, and is located just minutes from Point Lobos and Carmel Mission.

Famous Pebble Beach and 17-Mile Drive are close by, and visitors won't want to miss the shops of Carmel-by-the-Sea, the Monterey Bay Aquarium, Fisherman's Wharf, Cannery Row, Old Monterey, and more. Enjoy famous golf courses, hiking, and horseback riding, all minutes away from the Carmel Mission Inn.

3665 Rio Road at Highway One
Carmel, CA 93923
(831) 624-1841
(800) 348-9090
www.carmelmissioninn.com

ROOMS AVAILABLE	MAXIMUM SEATING	MAXIMUM STANDING	MAXIMUM THEATER
Carmelo Room	150	250	n/a
Tolosa Room	60	45	n/a
Dolores Room	60	110	n/a
Capistrano Room	40	64	n/a
Rio Room	20	30	n/a
Outdoor Facilities: Carmelo Patio	75	100	n/a

Exclusive Use of Indoor Facilities: *Available*

Exclusive Use of Outdoor Facilities: *Available*

Meeting Rooms: *5 meeting rooms with various capacities*

Availability of All Facilities: *Year-round*

Reserve for Events: *Varies*

Reserve for Meetings: *Varies*

Cocktail Parties Only: *Allowed*

Banquet Menu Prices Per Person (food only): *Luncheons $14.95-$19.95, Dinners $20.95-$32.95, Hors d'oeuvres from $4*

Buffet Menu Prices Per Person (food only): *Luncheons $16.95-$29.95, Dinners $25.95-$32.95, Hors d'oeuvres from $4*

Room Rental Fee/Deposits: *The room rental fee varies. The deposit amount also varies.*

Cancellation Policy: *Deposit refund varies. Cancellation policy varies.*

Credit Cards: *AMX, Visa, M/C, Dis, Diners*

Parking: *Lot, no charge*

Full-Service Bar: *Yes*

Corkage Fee: *$10*

Dance Floor: *Yes*

Wheelchair Accessible: *Yes*

Smoking Allowed: *No*

Live Music: *Yes*

Amplified Music: *Yes*

Event Coordination Services: *Yes*

Wedding Ceremony Allowed On-Site: *Yes*

Meeting Room Equipment: *Available upon request*

Sound System: *Yes*

Elevated Stage: *Yes*

Audio Visual: *Yes*

Restaurant Services: *Yes*

Catering Provided: *Yes*

HYO Caterer: *No*

Kitchen Facilities: *Hotel use only*

Linens, Silver, Glasses, etc. Provided: *Yes*

Tables and Chairs Provided: *Yes*

Wedding Cakes Baked In-House: *No*

In-House Florist: *No*

Overnight Accommodations: *165 guest rooms*

Hotel Discount for Guests of Event: *Negotiable*

Complimentary Hospitality Rooms: *Negotiable*

CARMEL VALLEY RANCH RESORT

Carmel Valley Ranch Resort is a Four Star/Four Diamond Golf and Tennis Resort. The one hundred forty-four guest suites feature wood-burning fireplaces and private decks. With country-side dining and an award-winning wine list, Carmel Valley Ranch has been a favorite destination for discriminating meeting planners since 1987.

Located on the sunny side of Carmel, with spectacular views of the valley below, The Ranch offers a variety of dining and meeting options for groups of ten to four hundred. The 3,200 square-foot ballroom divides up into eight separate rooms, each with its own air conditioning, lighting, and sound system. The Oak Tree courtyard features a rose-garden setting for a wedding or barbecue. The Executive Boardroom seats up to sixteen for special meetings or dining functions in a truly exclusive atmosphere.

One Old Ranch Road
Carmel, CA 93923
(831) 625-9500
www.wyndham.com

ROOMS AVAILABLE	MAXIMUM SEATING	MAXIMUM STANDING	MAXIMUM THEATER
Exec. Boardroom	16	20	n/a
Ballroom	220	280	340
Golf Club	130	200	n/a
Tennis Lawn Tent	280	400	n/a
Outdoor Facilities: Courtyard/Terrace	200	350	n/a

Exclusive Use of Entire Facilities: *Available*

Meeting Rooms: *The Ballroom can be broken down into 8 sections. There are 11 meeting rooms.*

Availability of All Facilities: *Year-round*

Reserve for Events: *3-6 months in advance*

Reserve for Meetings: *2-3 months in advance*

Cocktail Parties: *Allowed with minimum expenditure of $40 per person (excluding tax and tip)*

Banquet Menu Prices Per Person (food only): *Luncheons from $32.50, Dinners from $48, Hors d'oeuvres from $14.75*

Buffet Menu Prices Per Person (food only): *Luncheons from $28, Dinners from $63, Hors d'oeuvres from $44*

Room Rental Fee/Deposits: *The room rental fee varies from $100 to $5,000*

Cancellation Policy: *Deposit is nonrefundable*

Credit Cards: *AMX, Visa, M/C, Diners*

Parking: *Lot*

Full-Service Bar: *Yes*

Corkage Fee: *$15*

Dance Floor: *Yes*

Wheelchair Accessible: *Yes*

Smoking Allowed: *Outside*

Live Music: *Yes*

Amplified Music: *Yes*

Event Coordination Services: *Yes*

Wedding Ceremony Allowed On-Site: *Yes*

Meeting Room Equipment: *All*

Sound System: *Yes*

Elevated Stage: *Yes*

Audio Visual: *Yes*

Restaurant Services: *Yes*

Catering Provided: *Yes*

HYO Caterer: *No*

Kitchen Facilities: *No*

Linens, Silver, Glasses, etc. Provided: *Yes*

Tables and Chairs Provided: *Yes*

Wedding Cakes Baked In-House: *No*

In-House Florist: *No*

Overnight Accommodations: *144 guest suites*

Hotel Discount for Guests of Event: *Yes*

Complimentary Hospitality Rooms: *No*

The Gosby House Inn

$\mathcal{T}$ he Gosby House Inn is a cheerful two-story Victorian house painted light yellow with white trim and is an ideal location for small meetings, retreats, receptions, and ceremonies for up to thirty people.

Their attentive staff will tend to details and ensure a successful event. They offer twenty-two elegantly appointed guest rooms, and rates include a full gourmet breakfast.

Due to the intimate size of the Inn, event times vary. Please contact the innkeeper for further details.

643 Lighthouse
Pacific Grove, CA 93950
(831) 375-1287
www.foursisters.com

ROOMS AVAILABLE	MAXIMUM SEATING	MAXIMUM STANDING
Dining Room	14	n/a
Parlor	8	n/a
Outdoor Facilities	n/a	n/a
Exclusive Use of Entire Facility	22	35

Exclusive Use of Entire Facility: *Available*

Meeting Rooms: *None*

Availability of All Facilities: *Year-round*

Reserve for Events: *3 months in advance*

Cocktail Parties: *Prices quoted on request*

Banquet and Buffet Menu Prices Per Person (food only): *Prices quoted on request*

Room Rental Fee/Deposits: *The rental fee varies, but is usually about $300. The deposit ranges from $250 to $500.*

Cancellation Policy: *Deposit is refundable with 4 weeks' cancellation notice*

Credit Cards: *AMX, Visa, M/C*

Parking: *Street*

Full-Service Bar: *No, wine and Champagne only*

Corkage Fee: *$7.50*

Dance Floor: *No*

Wheelchair Accessible: *Yes*

Smoking Allowed: *No*

Live Music: *Yes*

Amplified Music: *No*

Event Coordination Services: *Yes*

Wedding Ceremony Allowed On-Site: *Yes (intimate groups)*

Meeting Room Equipment: *No*

Sound System: *No*

Elevated Stage: *No*

Audio Visual: *Yes*

Restaurant Services: *No*

Catering Provided: *Yes*

HYO Caterer: *No*

Kitchen Facilities: *No*

Linens, Silver, Glasses, etc. Provided: *Limited*

Tables and Chairs Provided: *Limited*

Wedding Cakes Baked In-House: *No*

In-House Florist: *No*

Overnight Accommodations: *22 guest rooms*

Hotel Discount for Guests of Event: *No*

Complimentary Hospitality Rooms: *No*

THE GREEN GABLES INN

he Green Gables Inn is a spectacular Victorian mansion overlooking the majestic Monterey Bay. Sweeping views of the dramatic shoreline are visible from almost every room in the house.

The Inn features eleven individually decorated guest rooms with lovely floral wallpapers, cozy quilts, and antique furniture.

Small gatherings of up to twenty-five people may be arranged using the dining room and adjoining parlor. The attentive staff will tend to the individual needs of your meeting or event, including customized catering.

Due to the intimate size of the Inn, event times are limited. Please contact the innkeeper for further details.

643 Lighthouse
Pacific Grove, CA 93950
(831) 375-2095
www.foursisters.com

ROOMS AVAILABLE	MAXIMUM SEATING	MAXIMUM STANDING
Exclusive Use of Entire Facility	24	20

Exclusive Use of Entire Facility: *Available*

Meeting Rooms: *None*

Availability of All Facilities: *Year-round*

Reserve for Events: *1 year in advance*

Cocktail Parties: *Allowed*

Banquet and Buffet Menu Prices Per Person (food only): *Prices quoted on request*

Room Rental Fee/Deposits: *The room rental fee is $500. The deposit is $500.*

Cancellation Policy: *Deposit is refundable with 6 weeks' cancellation notice*

Credit Cards: *AMX, Visa, M/C*

Parking: *Street*

Full-Service Bar: *No, wine and Champagne only*

Corkage Fee: *$5*

Dance Floor: *No*

Wheelchair Accessible: *No*

Smoking Allowed: *No*

Live Music: *Yes*

Amplified Music: *No*

Event Coordination Services: *Limited*

Wedding Ceremony Allowed On-Site: *Yes*

Meeting Room Equipment: *No*

Sound System: *No*

Elevated Stage: *No*

Audio Visual: *Yes*

Restaurant Services: *No*

Catering Provided: *Very limited*

HYO Caterer: *Yes*

Kitchen Facilities: *No*

Linens, Silver, Glasses, etc. Provided: *Limited*

Tables and Chairs Provided: *Limited*

Wedding Cakes Baked In-House: *No*

In-House Florist: *No*

Overnight Accommodations: *11 guest rooms*

Hotel Discount for Guests of Event: *No*

Complimentary Hospitality Rooms: *No*

*W*ith a spectacular setting at the gateway to Big Sur, Highlands Inn has excelled for many years at providing the ultimate in meeting rooms, whether for small groups or executive conference retreats of up to one hundred people.

Together, six individual rooms provide a total of 3,800 square feet of meeting space, all with uninterrupted glass-walled views of the rugged Carmel Highlands coastline. The meeting facilities have their own private entrance and luxuriously appointed boardroom decor.

An exceptional catering staff services the meeting facilities, equally efficient in business and social functions such as weddings, banquets, and receptions. Themes set a mood, and menus draw from the Monterey region's bounty of fresh fish, game, and produce.

Comfortable, sophisticated surroundings; attentive, courteous service; and spectacular views of the rugged coast are the ingredients of the Highlands Inn meeting experience.

Photo on Page P-6

HIGHLANDS INN
A PARK HYATT HOTEL

120 Highland Drive
Carmel, CA 93923
(831) 620-1234 Wedding Dept. (831) 622-5441
www.highlands-inn.com

ROOMS AVAILABLE	MAXIMUM SEATING	MAXIMUM STANDING
Wine Room (semiprivate	40	n/a
Surf Room (private)	120	130
Yankee Point Room (private)	50	50
Monarch Room (private)	15	15
Gazebo	95	140

Exclusive Use of Outdoor Facility: *Minimum food and beverage required. The fee is $750 for weddings under 25 persons.*

Meeting Rooms: *Six rooms including banquet rooms. The seating capacities vary.*

Availability of All Facilities: *Year-round*

Reserve for Events: *2-6 months in advance*

Reserve for Meetings: *6 months in advance*

Cocktail Parties: *Allowed with a minimum expenditure of $25 per person (excluding tax and tip)*

Banquet and Buffet Menu Prices Per Person (food only): *Luncheons from $35, Dinners from $55, Hors d'oeuvres from $24*

Room Rental Fee/Deposits: *The room rental fees are: Surf Room and Gazebo $3,000 (includes complimentary ocean-view spa suite), Yankee Point Room and Gazebo $1,650, Monarch Room and Gazebo $950. Room rental fee must be paid to reserve a room. Entire amount for event must be paid 1 month prior. Discounted off-seasonal rates available.*

Cancellation Policy: *Deposit is nonrefundable*

Credit Cards: *AMX, Visa, M/C, Dis*

Parking: *Lot, Valet*

Full-Service Bar: *Yes*

Corkage Fee: *$25*

Dance Floor: *Yes*

Wheelchair Accessible: *Partially*

Smoking Allowed: *No*

Live Music: *Yes, until midnight*

Amplified Music: *Yes*

Event Coordination Services: *Yes*

Wedding Ceremony On-Site: *Yes*

Meeting Room Equipment: *All*

Sound System: *Can be arranged*

Elevated Stage: *Can be arranged*

Audio Visual: *Can be arranged*

Restaurant Services: *Yes*

Catering Provided: *Yes, also for off-site events*

HYO Caterer: *No*

Kitchen Facilities: *Hotel use only*

Linens, Silver, Glasses, etc. Provided: *Yes*

Tables and Chairs Provided: *Yes*

Wedding Cakes Baked In-House: *Coordinated through hotel*

In-House Florist: *Coordinated through hotel*

Overnight Accommodations: *142 guest rooms*

Hotel Discount for Guests of Event: *Yes*

Complimentary Hospitality Rooms: *No*

*I*n 1998, the Hilton Monterey concluded over $7 million in renovations. The two-hundred-four-room full-service hotel is located in a beautiful garden setting. Each completely renovated and tastefully appointed guest room features a private patio, coffeemaker, two phones with speakerphone and dataport, high-speed Internet access, voicemail, hairdryer, iron and ironing board, remote control 25" TV, and in-room on-demand movies.

The newly renovated Pacific Grill restaurant features Early California Cuisine. Recreational facilities include two tennis courts, fitness room, putting green, table tennis, indoor whirlpool, and outdoor heated swimming pool. The hotel features meeting and banquet space for up to two hundred people.

Hotel guests enjoy morning newspapers, room service, guest laundry, valet service, and concierge service.

HILTON MONTEREY

1000 Aguajito Road
Monterey, CA 93940
(831) 373-6141
www.monterey.hilton.com

ROOMS AVAILABLE	MAXIMUM SEATING	MAXIMUM STANDING
Pacific Grill	96	n/a
Big Sur Room	175	250
Vista Del Mar Room	70	80
Peninsula Room	40	50
Presidio Room	100	100
Exclusive Use of Outdoor Facilities	200	200

Meeting Rooms: *4 meeting rooms that accommodate up to 200 guests*

Availability of All Facilities: *Year-round*

Reserve for Events: *Call for availability*

Reserve for Meetings: *Call for availability*

Cocktail Parties: *Allowed with a minimum expenditure of $12 per person first hour (excluding tax and tip)*

Banquet Menu Prices Per Person (food only): *Luncheons $15-$20, Dinners $25-$37, Hors d'oeuvres $20-$40*

Buffet Menu Prices Per Person (food only): *Luncheons $16-$25, Dinners $25-$37, Hors d'oeuvres from $20-$40*

Room Rental Fee/Deposits: *The rental fee ranges from $200 to $500. The deposit is 50% of the estimated total expenditure.*

Cancellation Policy: *Deposit is refundable with 4 weeks' cancellation notice*

Credit Cards: *AMX, Visa, M/C, Dis*

Parking: *Lot, Street*

Full-Service Bar: *Yes*

Corkage Fee: *$10*

Dance Floor: *Yes*

Wheelchair Accessible: *Yes*

Smoking Allowed: *No*

Live Music: *Yes*

Amplified Music: *Yes*

Event Coordination Services: *Yes*

Wedding Ceremony Allowed On-Site: *Yes*

Meeting Room Equipment: *Yes*

Sound System: *Yes*

Elevated Stage: *Yes*

Audio Visual: *Yes*

Restaurant Services: *Yes*

Catering Provided: *Yes*

HYO Caterer: *No*

Kitchen Facilities: *No*

Linens, Silver, Glasses, etc. Provided: *Yes*

Tables and Chairs Provided: *Yes*

Wedding Cakes Baked In-House: *No*

In-House Florist: *No*

Overnight Accommodations: *204 guest rooms*

HYATT REGENCY MONTEREY

*T*he Hyatt Regency Monterey is located at the heart of the Monterey Peninsula near Cannery Row, the Monterey Bay Aquarium, Fisherman's Wharf, and shopping in Carmel-by-the-Sea. Overlooking Pebble Beach Company's historic Del Monte Golf Course, the Hyatt suits all of its guests to a tee in accommodations, dining, and guest services.

The five-hundred-seventy-five-room convention hotel includes garden rooms, suites and Regency Club guest rooms and is home to the largest amount of hotel conference space between San Jose and Los Angeles.

1 Old Golf Course Drive
Monterey, CA 93940
(831) 372-1234
www.montereyhyatt.com

ROOMS AVAILABLE	MAXIMUM BANQUET	MAXIMUM RECEPTION	MAXIMUM THEATER
Monterey Grand Ballroom	650	750	800
Regency Grand Ballroom	1,000	1,200	1,200
Oaktree Room	60	80	80
Cypress Room	130	160	200
Windjammer Room	150	160	150
Outdoor Facilities	350	400	n/a

Meeting Rooms: *35 rooms that seat up to 2,890 guests*

Availability of All Facilities: *Year-round*

Reserve for Events: *Yes*

Reserve for Meetings: *Yes*

Cocktail Parties: *Allowed. Minimum expenditure is $450.*

Banquet Menu Prices Per Person (food only): *Luncheons from $23, Dinners from $34, Hors d'oeuvres from $2.75*

Buffet Menu Prices Per Person (food only): *Luncheons from $27, Dinners from $44, Hors d'oeuvres from $2.75*

Room Rental Fee/Deposits: *The room rental fee varies from $100 to $8,000 depending on the size of the room*

Cancellation Policy: *Varies*

Credit Cards: *AMX, Visa, M/C, Dis, Diners*

Parking: *Complimentary*

Full-Service Bar: *Yes*

Corkage Fee: *$10*

Dance Floor: *Yes*

Wheelchair Accessible: *Yes*

Smoking Allowed: *In designated areas*

Live Music: *Yes*

Amplified Music: *In designated areas*

Event Coordination Services: *Yes*

Wedding Ceremony Allowed On-Site: *Yes*

Meeting Room Equipment: *All*

Sound System: *Yes*

Elevated Stage: *Yes*

Audio Visual: *Yes*

Restaurant Services: *Yes*

Catering Provided: *Yes*

HYO Caterer: *No*

Kitchen Facilities: *Hotel use only*

Linens, Silver, Glasses, etc. Provided: *Yes*

Tables and Chairs Provided: *Yes*

Wedding Cakes Baked In-House: *No*

In-House Florist: *No*

Overnight Accommodations: *575 guest rooms*

Hotel Discount for Guests of Event: *Negotiable*

Complimentary Hospitality Rooms: *No*

The Inn at Spanish Bay

*N*estled between the Del Monte Forest and the Pacific shore, The Inn and Links at Spanish Bay offer a luxurious enclave for golf enthusiasts and relaxation seekers alike. Surrounding the Inn, the classic Scottish-style linksland course promises championship play amid grassy, windswept dunes sloping to the sea. An eight-court Tennis Pavilion, a full-service fitness club, fine restaurants and boutiques, and attentive personal service round out the exemplary offerings at this world-class resort.

The Inn provides over 14,000 square feet of meeting and banquet space, much of it offering panoramic views of the Pacific. A stunning ballroom, with a capacity of eight hundred, features a separate entrance and a lovely indoor/outdoor prefunction promenade. Five additional rooms have capacities ranging from ten to two hundred fifty.

2700 17-Mile Drive
Pebble Beach, CA 93953
(831) 647-7500
www.pebblebeach.com

ROOMS AVAILABLE	MAXIMUM BANQUET	MAXIMUM RECEPTION	MAXIMUM THEATER
Ballroom	350	800	1,000
St. Andrews Ballroom	170	300	250
Royal Troon Room	80	100	120
Ballroom Gallery	n/a	500	n/a
Fairway Patio	120	250	n/a

Meeting Rooms: *16 rooms that seat from 10 to 700 guests*

Availability of All Facilities: *Year-round*

Reserve for Events: *3-6 months in advance*

Reserve for Meetings: *3-6 months in advance*

Cocktail Parties: *Allowed with a minimum expenditure of $40 per person*

Banquet Menu Prices Per Person (food only): *Luncheons from $27, Dinners from $55, Hors d'oeuvres from $20*

Buffet Menu Prices Per Person (food only): *Luncheons from $26, Dinners from $60, Hors d'oeuvres from $40*

Room Rental Fee/Deposits: *The room rental fee ranges from $300 to $3,000. The deposit varies.*

Cancellation Policy: *Deposit is nonrefundable*

Credit Cards: *All major credit cards*

Parking: *Lot, Valet*

Full-Service Bar: *Yes*

Corkage Fee: *Yes*

Dance Floor: *Yes, call for price*

Wheelchair Accessible: *Yes*

Smoking Allowed: *No*

Live Music: *Yes*

Amplified Music: *Yes*

Event Coordination Services: *Yes*

Wedding Ceremony Allowed On-Site: *Yes*

Meeting Room Equipment: *All*

Sound System: *Yes*

Elevated Stage: *Yes*

Audio Visual: *Yes*

Restaurant Services: *Yes*

Catering Provided: *Yes*

HYO Caterer: *No*

Kitchen Facilities: *For hotel use only*

Linens, Silver, Glasses, etc. Provided: *Yes*

Tables and Chairs Provided: *Yes*

Wedding Cakes Baked In-House: *Yes*

In-House Florist: *Yes*

Overnight Accommodations: *270 guest rooms*

Hotel Discount for Guests of Event: *No*

Complimentary Hospitality Rooms: *No*

La Playa Hotel

La Playa Hotel is an unsurpassed location for corporate meetings, weddings or special events. The famous white-sand Carmel Beach is just two blocks away, and the picturesque town, with its art galleries, boutiques, and restaurants, is only four blocks away.

Originally built in 1904, the Mediterranean-style artist's mansion is the only full-service resort hotel in Carmel-by-the-Sea. Guest rooms are appointed with hand-carved furniture featuring La Playa's mermaid motif and afford views of the ocean, garden patio, or residential Carmel.

Conference and banquet facilities can accommodate from ten to one hundred ten guests, and the garden gazebo is ideal for wedding ceremonies. In a picture-perfect setting amidst oceans of flowers and cypress, La Playa's staff will oversee every detail of your event from start to finish.

Photo on Page P-8

8th and Camino Real
P.O. Box 900
Carmel, CA 93921
(831) 624-6476 (800) 582-8900
www.laplayahotel.com

ROOMS AVAILABLE	MAXIMUM SEATING	MAXIMUM STANDING
Poseidon Room	112	150
Carmel Room	56	70
Garden Room	40	40
Fireside Room	16	n/a
Patio Room	10	n/a
Gazebo (weddings only)	85	112

Exclusive Use of Outdoor Facility: *Reception must follow at hotel*

Meeting Rooms: *5 meeting rooms that can seat up to 110 guests*

Availability of All Facilities: *Year-round*

Reserve for Events: *12 months in advance*

Reserve for Meetings: *3-6 months in advance*

Cocktail Parties: *Allowed with a minimum expenditure of $25 per person (excluding tax and tip)*

Banquet Menu Prices Per Person (food only): *Luncheons $21-$26, Dinners $28-$42, Hors d'oeuvres from $33 per dozen*

Buffet Menu Prices Per Person (food only): *Luncheons $23-$28, Dinners $34-$45, Hors d'oeuvres from $33 per dozen*

Room Rental Fee/Deposits: *Room rental fee ranges from $500 to $1,500. The deposit for weddings is $2,000.*

Cancellation Policy: *Deposit is nonrefundable*

Credit Cards: *AMX, Visa, M/C, Diners*

Parking: *Street, Valet, Small Lot*

Full-Service Bar: *Yes*

Corkage Fee: *n/a*

Dance Floor: *Yes*

Wheelchair Accessible: *Yes*

Smoking Allowed: *No*

Live Music: *Restricted*

Amplified Music: *Restricted*

Event Coordination Services: *Yes*

Wedding Ceremony Allowed On-Site: *Yes*

Meeting Room Equipment: *All*

Sound System: *Yes*

Elevated Stage: *No*

Audio Visual: *Yes, outside company*

Restaurant Services: *Yes*

Catering Provided: *Yes*

HYO Caterer: *No*

Kitchen Facilities: *Hotel use only*

Linens, Silver, Glasses, etc. Provided: *Yes*

Tables and Chairs Provided: *Yes*

Wedding Cakes Baked In-House: *Yes*

In-House Florist: *No*

Overnight Accommodations: *75 guest rooms, 5 cottages*

Hotel Discount for Guests of Event: *No*

Complimentary Hospitality Rooms: *Yes*

THE LODGE AT PEBBLE BEACH

he Lodge's tradition of relaxed elegance in a stunning natural setting has earned it an international reputation for exceptional hospitality. With award-winning restaurants; superb accommodations; extensive equestrian, tennis, and fitness facilities; and a promenade of fine boutiques, The Lodge provides something for everyone.

For group functions, unique opportunities abound—ranging from Clambake Parties to private wine tastings with California wineries.

Meeting facilities include nine major rooms with capacities of up to four hundred. In addition to a flexible conference center overlooking The Lodge and its surrounding gardens, there are a ballroom and several reception salons, including the chandeliered Library and the intimate Card Room with adjoining sea-vista Terrace.

The Lodge at Pebble Beach is a consistent winner of the prestigious McRand Award for conference excellence.

17-Mile Drive
Pebble Beach, CA 93953
(831) 624-3811
www.pebblebeach.com

ROOMS AVAILABLE	MAXIMUM BANQUET	MAXIMUM RECEPTION	MAXIMUM THEATER
Conference Center	300	500	400
Pebble Beach Room	180	250	250
Library	60	80	65
Card Room	30	50	35
Stanton Room	24	40	n/a
18th Lawn Ceremony Only	n/a	n/a	350

Meeting Rooms: *9 rooms that seat from 10 to 300 guests*

Availability of All Facilities: *Year-round*

Reserve for Events: *6 months in advance*

Reserve for Meetings: *6 months in advance*

Cocktail Parties: *Allowed with a minimum expenditure of $40 per person (excluding tax and tip)*

Banquet Menu Prices Per Person (food only): *Luncheons $27-$40, Dinners $55-$110, Hors d'oeuvres $20-$40*

Buffet Menu Prices Per Person (food only): *Luncheons $27.50-$40, Dinners $70-$100, Hors d'oeuvres $20-$40*

Room Rental Fee/Deposits: *The room rental fee ranges from $800 to $2,000. The room rental fee acts as a deposit.*

Cancellation Policy: *Deposit is nonrefundable*

Credit Cards: *All major credit cards*

Parking: *Lot, Valet*

Full-Service Bar: *Yes*

Corkage Fee: *Yes, call for price*

Dance Floor: *Yes*

Wheelchair Accessible: *Yes*

Smoking Allowed: *No*

Live Music: *Yes*

Amplified Music: *Yes*

Event Coordination Services: *Yes*

Wedding Ceremony Allowed On-Site: *Yes*

Meeting Room Equipment: *Available*

Sound System: *Yes*

Elevated Stage: *Yes*

Audio Visual: *Available*

Restaurant Services: *Yes*

Catering Provided: *Yes*

HYO Caterer: *No*

Kitchen Facilities: *No*

Linens, Silver, Glasses, etc. Provided: *Yes*

Tables and Chairs Provided: *Yes*

Wedding Cakes Baked In-House: *No*

In-House Florist: *No*

Overnight Accommodations: *31 guest rooms*

Hotel Discount for Guests of Event: *No*

Complimentary Hospitality Rooms: *No*

*L*ike vintage wine, Los Laureles gets better with time. Rich in legend and history, the Lodge and restaurant reflect the colorful influence of Spanish conquistadors, tribal Indians, and a flavorful mixture of bandits, cowboys, and socialites.

Nestled deep in the lush Carmel Valley, Los Laureles basks in warm, brilliant sunshine miles away from coastal fog. The deep-blue sky, often etched by feathery white clouds, provides the perfect backdrop for swimming, picnicking, hiking, or simply relaxing under a shady oak tree.

A bright, sun-filled meeting room for groups from ten to fifty looks out onto a backyard of colorful flowers and shady trees... perfect for more productive meetings. Full meeting services and equipment are available.

The tradition, the history, the charm, and the atmosphere of Los Laureles will never be bottled. For them, every year is a vintage year. So come taste and savor these unique experiences soon.

LOS LAURELES LODGE
AN HISTORIC AMERICAN COUNTRY INN

313 W. Carmel Valley Road
Carmel Valley, CA 93924
(831) 659-2233
www.loslaureles.com

ROOMS AVAILABLE	MAXIMUM SEATING	MAXIMUM STANDING
Terrace Room	40	50
Library	16	25
Oak Room	20	24
Terrace Garden	150	200

Exclusive Use of Outdoor Facility: *Available*

Meeting Rooms: *4 meeting rooms available that can seat from 10 to 40 guests*

Availability of All Facilities: *Year-round*

Reserve for Events: *1 month in advance*

Reserve for Meetings: *1 month in advance*

Cocktail Parties: *Allowed with a negotiable minimum expenditure per person*

Banquet Menu Prices Per Person (food only): *Negotiable*

Buffet Menu Prices Per Person (food only): *Negotiable*

Room Rental Fees/Deposits: *The room rental fee is negotiable. The deposit varies.*

Cancellation Policy: *Deposit is refundable with 90 days' cancellation notice*

Credit Cards: *AMX, Visa, M/C*

Parking: *Lot*

Full-Service Bar: *Yes*
Corkage Fee: *Yes, call for price*
Dance Floor: *Available*
Wheelchair Accessible: *Yes*
Smoking Allowed: *No*
Live Music: *Yes*
Amplified Music: *Yes*

Event Coordination Services: *Yes*
Wedding Ceremony Allowed On-Site: *Yes*
Meeting Room Equipment: *Available*
Sound System: *Available*
Elevated Stage: *Yes*
Audio Visual: *Available*
Restaurant Services: *Yes*
Catering Provided: *Yes*
HYO Caterer: *No*
Kitchen Facilities: *No*
Linens, Silver, Glasses, etc. Provided: *Yes*
Tables and Chairs Provided: *Yes*
Wedding Cakes Baked In-House: *No*
In-House Florist: *Available*
Overnight Accommodations: *31 guest rooms*
Hotel Discount for Guests of Event: *Yes*
Complimentary Hospitality Rooms: *Yes*

THE MARTINE INN

This gracious mansion sits atop the cliffs of Pacific Grove overlooking the rocky coastline of Monterey Bay. The splendid facilities include an enclosed land-scaped courtyard, a library with a fireplace and an inlaid hardwood dance floor, a party room, and parlor, dining, and sitting rooms with ocean views.

Meals at the Inn are served on fine porcelain, Victorian and Old Sheffield silver, lace, and Lancaster Rose sterling-silver flatware made by Gorham in the 1890s.

For a beautiful, unique wedding, an experienced on-staff consultant will help you create the perfect atmosphere, right down to the flowers, photographer, food, and music.

Intimate conference groups are catered to on an individual basis: meeting rooms of preference are selected, custom menus are planned, and luxurious bedrooms are given to all attendees.

Make a personal statement of your individuality in this elegant Victorian setting.

Photo on Page P-9

255 Ocean View Boulevard
Pacific Grove, CA 93950
(831) 373-3388
(800) 862-5588
www.martineinn.com

ROOMS AVAILABLE	MAXIMUM SEATING	MAXIMUM STANDING
Main Dining Room	12	20
Parlor	40	60
Conference Room	20	30
Library	n/a	20
Outdoor Facilities	125	125

Exclusive Use of Entire Facility: *If there are over 50 guests, the entire Inn must be booked*

Meeting Rooms: *6 meeting rooms of varying sizes that can seat from 6 to 50 people*

Availability of All Facilities: *Year-round*

Reserve for Events: *1-6 months in advance*

Reserve for Meetings: *1-6 months in advance*

Cocktail Parties: *Allowed with minimum expenditure per person*

Banquet and Buffet Menu Prices Per Person (food only): *Luncheons from $45, Dinners from $55, Hors d'oeuvres from $15*

Room Rental Fee/Deposits: *Room rental fee varies from $500 to $950. A fee is required to reserve a date.*

Cancellation Policy: *Fees are nonrefundable. Guest rooms and food are refundable with 30 days' cancellation notice.*

Credit Cards: *AMX, Visa, M/C, Dis*

Parking: *Lot, Street*

Full-Service Bar: *Yes*

Corkage Fee: *$15*

Dance Floor: *Yes*

Wheelchair Accessible: *Yes*

Smoking Allowed: *Yes, outside*

Live Music: *Yes*

Amplified Music: *Yes*

Event Coordination Services: *Yes*

Wedding Ceremony Allowed On-Site: *Yes*

Meeting Room Equipment: *Yes*

Sound System: *No*

Elevated Stage: *No*

Audio Visual: *Yes*

Restaurant Services: *No*

Catering Provided: *Yes*

HYO Caterer: *No*

Kitchen Facilities: *No*

Linens, Silver, Glasses, etc. Provided: *Yes*

Tables and Chairs Provided: *Yes*

Wedding Cakes Baked In-House: *Yes*

In-House Florist: *No*

Overnight Accommodations: *24 guest rooms*

Hotel Discount for Guests of Event: *No*

Complimentary Hospitality Rooms: *No*

Mission Ranch

*M*ission Ranch was built in the 1850s. This historic property has a quiet, peaceful ambiance perfect for a classic wedding in a country setting. The award-winning grounds offer views of hillsides, meadows, and Carmel River Beach.

The original structures on the property were renovated ten years ago. The Patio Barn offers carpeting, a built-in dance floor, a stage, and a long copper-topped bar. Floor-to-ceiling glass doors open onto a patio with sweeping views of meadows leading to Carmel River Beach. The Large Barn has a three-story open-beam ceiling, carpeting, a built-in dance floor, a portable stage, and a small bar area.

Photo on Page P-10

26270 Dolores
Carmel, CA 93923
(831) 624-3824

ROOMS AVAILABLE	MAXIMUM SEATING	MAXIMUM STANDING
Large Barn	180	225
Patio Party Barn	112	150
Meeting Room	12	n/a
Outdoor Facilities	n/a	n/a

Meeting Rooms: *1 room that seats 12 guests*

Availability of All Facilities: *Year-round*

Reserve for Events: *12 months in advance*

Reserve for Meetings: *3 months in advance*

Cocktail Parties: *Allowed*

Banquet and Buffet Menu Prices Per Person (food only): *Luncheons from $30, Dinners from $35, Hors d'oeuvres from $25*

Room Rental Fee/Deposits: *The room rental fees are: Large Barn $1,000 and Patio Party Barn $1,500. Rental fee acts as deposit.*

Cancellation Policy: *Deposit is nonrefundable*

Credit Cards: *AMX, Visa, M/C*

Parking: *Lot, Street*

Full-Service Bar: *Yes*

Corkage Fee: *$15*

Dance Floor: *Yes*

Wheelchair Accessible: *Yes*

Smoking Allowed: *No*

Live Music: *Yes*

Amplified Music: *Yes, inside only*

Event Coordination Services: *Yes*

Wedding Ceremony Allowed On-Site: *Yes*

Meeting Room Equipment: *Yes*

Sound System: *Yes, limited*

Elevated Stage: *Yes*

Audio Visual: *Yes, limited*

Restaurant Services: *Yes*

Catering Provided: *Yes*

HYO Caterer: *No*

Kitchen Facilities: *No*

Linens, Silver, Glasses, etc. Provided: *Yes*

Tables and Chairs Provided: *Yes*

Wedding Cakes Baked In-House: *No*

In-House Florist: *Yes*

Overnight Accommodations: *31 guest rooms*

Hotel Discount for Guests of Event: *No*

Complimentary Hospitality Rooms: *No*

MONTEREY CONFERENCE CENTER

The Monterey Conference Center is located in downtown Monterey, just steps away from scenic Old Fisherman's Wharf. It adjoins the Doubletree, Monterey Marriott, and Hotel Pacific hotels and offers three levels of unsurpassed facilities for discerning professional groups and associations.

Their 58,000 square feet include the Serra Exhibit Hall/Ballroom, the plush five-hundred-seat Steinbeck Forum theater, divisible meeting rooms, luxurious boardrooms, sunny terraces and patios, and complete banquet facilities.

An ideal location and outstanding facilities alone do not assure the success of your event. The Monterey Conference Center is proud to add its dedicated staff, acknowledged for outstanding service by industry leaders. The combination of location, facilities, and an award-winning staff has gained the Monterey Conference Center a most distinguished client roster.

One Portola Plaza
Monterey, CA 93940
(831) 646-3770
www.meet-in-monterey.com

ROOMS AVAILABLE	MAXIMUM SEATING	MAXIMUM STANDING	MAXIMUM THEATER
Serra Ballroom	1,300	2,000	2,300
De Anza Ballroom	750	1,000	1,000
Steinbeck Forum	n/a	n/a	490
Ferrante Room	150	200	220
Colton Room	100	150	150
Outdoor Facilities: Jeffers Plaza	200	800	n/a

Exclusive Use of Outdoor Facilities: *No*

Meeting Rooms: *15 meeting rooms that seat up to 2,300 guest*

Availability of All Facilities: *Year-round*

Reserve for Events: *3 months in advance*

Reserve for Meetings: *3 months in advance*

Cocktail Parties: *Reserve 3 months in advance*

Banquet Menu Prices Per Person (food only): *Luncheons $12.75-$17.25, Dinners $18.75-$34.95, Hors d'oeuvres vary*

Buffet Menu Prices Per Person (food only): *Luncheons $18.75 $29.95, Dinners $24.95-$35.95, Hors d'oeuvres vary*

Room Rental Fee/Deposits: *The room rental fee varies. The deposit amount also varies.*

Cancellation Policy: *Deposit is nonrefundable*

Credit Cards: *AMX, Visa, M/C*

Parking: *City Garage, Fee*

Full-Service Bar: *Yes*

Corkage Fee: *Yes, call for price*

Dance Floor: *Yes*

Wheelchair Accessible: *Yes*

Smoking Allowed: *No*

Live Music: *Yes*

Amplified Music: *Yes*

Event Coordination Services: *Yes*

Wedding Ceremony Allowed On-Site: *Yes*

Meeting Room Equipment: *Complete*

Sound System: *Yes*

Elevated Stage: *Yes*

Audio Visual: *Yes*

Restaurant Services: *No*

Catering Provided: *Yes*

HYO Caterer: *No*

Kitchen Facilities: *No*

Linens, Silver, Glasses, etc. Provided: *Yes*

Tables and Chairs Provided: *Yes*

Wedding Cakes Baked In-House: *No*

In-House Florist: *No*

Overnight Accommodations: *No*

*P*erched atop the tallest building in town, framed by floor-to-ceiling windows and boasting Monterey's most breathtaking view, Ferrante's Bayview is a banquet space as special as your wedding. Outside the windows, light glitters off the Monterey Bay in romantic accompaniment to the magic of your day. Inside, the spacious, comfortable, warm facility reflects all the service and care you expect from the Monterey Marriott Hotel.

Ferrante's Bayview offers complete wedding coordination, including full-service catering, a wide selection of wedding packages, and even assistance in securing bands, florists, and other services. The hall holds more than two hundred people with room for a dance floor and band or disk jockey, making it both generous in size and intimate in effect. Available every day and evening, Ferrante's Bayview can accommodate almost any wedding party and any need.

It's your day...why not spend it on top of the world?

Photo on Page P-11

Monterey Marriott

350 Calle Principal
Monterey, CA 93940
(831) 647-4005
www.marriott.com/mryca

ROOMS AVAILABLE	MAXIMUM BANQUET	MAXIMUM RECEPTION	MAXIMUM THEATER
San Carlos Ballroom	600	800	1,200
Ferrantes Bayview	250	400	n/a
Various Rooms	50	50	n/a
Memory Gardens	400	600	n/a

Meeting Rooms: *14 rooms that seat up to 600 guests*

Availability of All Facilities: *Year-round*

Reserve for Events: *Up to 1 year in advance*

Reserve for Meetings: *Up to 1 year in advance*

Cocktail Parties: *Allowed with a minimum expenditure of $10 per person (excluding tax and tip)*

Banquet Menu Prices Per Person (food only): *Luncheons $20-$35, Dinners $35-$53, Hors d'oeuvres $10-$20*

Buffet Menu Prices Per Person (food only): *Luncheons $23-$57, Dinners $35-$57, Hors d'oeuvres $10-$20*

Room Rental Fee/Deposits: *The room rental fee varies. The deposit is 10% of the estimated total expenditure.*

Cancellation Policy: *Deposit is nonrefundable*

Credit Cards: *All major credit cards*

Parking: *Street, Valet*

Full-Service Bar: *Yes*

Corkage Fee: *Yes, call for price*

Dance Floor: *Yes*

Wheelchair Accessible: *Yes*

Smoking Allowed: *No*

Live Music: *Yes*

Amplified Music: *Yes*

Event Coordination Services: *Yes*

Wedding Ceremony Allowed On-Site: *Yes*

Meeting Room Equipment: *Yes*

Sound System: *Yes*

Elevated Stage: *Yes*

Audio Visual: *Yes*

Restaurant Services: *Yes*

Catering Provided: *Yes*

HYO Caterer: *No*

Kitchen Facilities: *No*

Linens, Silver, Glasses, etc. Provided: *Yes*

Tables and Chairs Provided: *Yes*

Wedding Cakes Baked In-House: *No*

In-House Florist: *No*

Overnight Accommodations: *341 guest rooms*

Hotel Discount for Guests of Event: *Yes, based on availability*

Complimentary Hospitality Rooms: *No*

THE MONTEREY PLAZA HOTEL & SPA

The Monterey Plaza Hotel sits dramatically over the water, providing an inspirational setting for both indoor and outdoor functions, including meetings, banquets, wedding ceremonies, and receptions.

Sun-splashed ceremonies take place on either of the the hotel's two terraces. Both have panoramic views of the Pacific and require minimum decoration. On the Lower Terrace, the bride will capture every eye as she descends the main staircase, while on the Upper Plaza, the processional will walk beneath a white trellis set off by flower-filled terra-cotta planters.

The latest and most exciting development is the addition of a full-service European-style oceanfront health spa and four luxury suites featuring fireplaces and outdoor decks. Now you can indulge in a relaxing massage, facial, or sauna before (or even after) your event. The large luxury suites can be used for intimate celebrations, dinners or cocktail parties.

Photo on Page P-12

400 Cannery Row
Monterey, CA 93940
(831) 646-1700
www.montereyplazahotel.com

ROOMS AVAILABLE	MAXIMUM BANQUET	MAXIMUM RECEPTION	MAXIMUM THEATER
Cypress Ballroom	270	480	480
Dolphin Room	180	435	435
Monterey Bay Room	120	200	200
OUTDOOR FACILITIES			
Upper Plaza	350	600	n/a
Lower Plaza	70	200	n/a

Exclusive Use of Outdoor Facilities: *n/a*

Meeting Rooms: *10 meeting rooms that can seat from 2 to 480 guests*

Availability of All Facilities: *Year-round*

Reserve for Events: *15 days to 1 year in advance*

Reserve for Meetings: *60 days in advance*

Cocktail Parties: *Allowed. Minimum expenditure per person is negotiable.*

Banquet Menu Prices Per Person (food only): *Luncheons from $26, Dinners from $56, Hors d'oeuvres: open*

Buffet Menu Prices Per Person (food only): *Luncheons from $32, Dinners from $60, Hors d'oeuvres open*

Room Rental Fees/Deposits: *The room rental fee ranges from $350-$1,400. The deposit is equal to room rental fee.*

Cancellation Policy: *Deposit is nonrefundable*

Credit Cards: *AMX, Visa, M/C, Dis, Diners, CB*

Parking: *Valet, Lot, Street*

Full-Service Bar: *Yes*

Corkage Fee: *n/a*

Dance Floor: *Yes*

Wheelchair Accessible: *Yes*

Smoking Allowed: *No*

Live Music: *Yes*

Amplified Music: *Yes*

Event Coordination Services: *Yes*

Wedding Ceremony Allowed On-Site: *Yes*

Meeting Room Equipment: *All*

Sound System: *Yes*

Elevated Stage: *Yes*

Audio Visual: *Yes*

Restaurant Services: *Yes*

Catering Provided: *Yes*

HYO Caterer: *No*

Kitchen Facilities: *No*

Linens, Silver, Glasses, etc. Provided: *Yes*

Tables and Chairs Provided: *Yes*

Wedding Cakes Baked In-House: *Yes*

In-House Florist: *No*

Overnight Accommodations: *290 guest rooms*

Hotel Discount for Guests of Event: *n/a*

Complimentary Hospitality Rooms: *n/a*

QUAIL LODGE RESORT AND GOLF CLUB

Nestled in the rolling hills of beautiful Carmel and framed by graceful willows, Quail Lodge Resort and Golf Club has much to offer. Wedding vows may be exchanged beside a sparkling lake with nature's beauty all around, and you may stage the reception in a festive tent or elegant party room.

Picturesque settings such as the arched bridge at Mallard Lake or the rolling lawns of Quail Meadows are among the favorite locations for weddings. Meeting rooms are available for group functions from two to three hundred, most with splendid views of lakes, gardens, or fairways. Wind down your meetings with a relaxing round of golf on our championship course.

Our innovative and talented chefs are only too happy to create menus designed especially for you. From lavish buffets and elegant formal dinners at the expansive Country Club to small, intimate gatherings at the award-winning Covey Restaurant, every detail is important to us.

Photo on Page P-15

8205 Valley Greens Drive
Carmel, CA 93923
(831) 624-2888
www.peninsula.com

ROOMS AVAILABLE	MAXIMUM SEATING	MAXIMUM STANDING	MAXIMUM THEATER
The Covey Restaurant	92	n/a	n/a
Fairway Room	70	90	150
Garden Room	50	50	50
Club Dining Room	250	400	300
Valley Room	80	90	130
Outdoor Facilities	500	n/a	n/a

Exclusive Use of Outdoor Facilities: *Available*

Meeting Rooms: *8 meeting rooms with various capacities*

Availability of All Facilities: *Year-round*

Reserve for Events: *1 month in advance*

Reserve for Meetings: *1 month in advance*

Cocktail Parties: *Allowed*

Banquet Menu Prices Per Person (food only): *Luncheons $26-$35, Dinners $45-$65, Hors d'oeuvres from $10*

Buffet Menu Prices Per Person (food only): *Luncheons $25-$40, Dinners $65, Hors d'oeuvres from $10*

Room Rental Fee/Deposits: *The room rental fee varies from $250 to $2,500. The deposit amount also varies.*

Cancellation Policy: *Deposit is nonrefundable*

Credit Cards: *AMX, Visa, M/C, Diners*

Parking: *Lot*

Full-Service Bar: *Yes*

Corkage Fee: *$15*

Dance Floor: *Yes*

Wheelchair Accessible: *Yes*

Smoking Allowed: *No*

Live Music: *Yes*

Amplified Music: *Yes*

Event Coordination Services: *Yes*

Wedding Ceremony Allowed On-Site: *Yes*

Meeting Room Equipment: *Yes*

Sound System: *Yes*

Elevated Stage: *Yes*

Audio Visual: *Yes*

Restaurant Services: *Yes*

Catering Provided: *Yes*

HYO Caterer: *No*

Kitchen Facilities: *No*

Linens, Silver, Glasses, etc. Provided: *Yes*

Tables and Chairs Provided: *Yes*

Wedding Cakes Baked In-House: *No*

In-House Florist: *Yes*

Overnight Accommodations: *97 guest rooms*

Hotel Discount for Guests of Event: *10 or more rooms, subject to availability*

Complimentary Hospitality Rooms: *No*

STONEPINE ESTATE RESORT

Ideal for limited business affairs or affairs of the heart, this secluded three-hundred-thirty-acre resort in Carmel Valley offers the ultimate retreat from the realities of everyday life.

Once the country home of the Crocker banking family, Stonepine now offers fourteen luxurious suites that may be booked individually or on an exclusive basis. The main house, built from 1927 to 1929, is reminiscent of a French chateau or northern-Italian villa. In addition to the formal Living Room, Dining Room, and Library, the eight luxurious suites at the Chateau Noel enjoy proximity to the gardens, swimming pool, tennis courts and workout room.

The surrounding woodlands of Stonepine include a 3.5-mile riding and hiking trail along the Santa Lucia mountains and the Carmel River. Each suite at Stonepine has a unique decor and ambiance, from the Champagne decor of the Taittinger Suite, to their newest edition, Hermes House, decorated in the true spirit of Hermes.

150 East Carmel Valley Road
Carmel Valley, CA 93924
(831) 659-2245
www.stonepinecalifornia.com

ROOMS AVAILABLE	MAXIMUM SEATING	MAXIMUM STANDING
Main Dining Room	32	n/a
Petite Dining Room	8	n/a
Living Room	n/a	100
Chateau Lawn	200	200
Equestrian Club House Lawn	250	250

Exclusive Use of Entire Facility: *Available*

Meeting Rooms: *4 meeting rooms that seat up to 20 guests*

Availability of All Facilities: *Year-round*

Reserve for Events: *6-12 months in advance*

Reserve for Meetings: *3-6 months in advance*

Cocktail Parties: *Can be arranged*

Banquet Menu Prices Per Person (food only): *Luncheons average $30 per person, Dinners from $65, Hors d'oeuvres from $12*

Buffet Menu Prices Per Person (food only): *n/a*

Room Rental Fee/Deposits: *The room rental fee varies. The deposit also varies.*

Cancellation Policy: *Deposit is refundable with 4 months' notice*

Credit Cards: *AMX, Visa, M/C*

Parking: *Valet, Self-park*

Full-Service Bar: *Allowed*

Corkage Fee: *$15*

Dance Floor: *Can be arranged*

Wheelchair Accessible: *Yes*

Smoking Allowed: *No*

Live Music: *Yes*

Amplified Music: *Yes*

Event Coordination Services: *Yes*

Wedding Ceremony Allowed On-Site: *Yes*

Meeting Room Equipment: *Can be arranged*

Sound System: *Can be arranged*

Elevated Stage: *Can be arranged*

Audio Visual: *Yes*

Restaurant Services: *No*

Catering Provided: *Yes*

HYO Caterer: *No*

Kitchen Facilities: *No*

Linens, Silver, Glasses, etc. Provided: *Can be arranged*

Tables and Chairs Provided: *Can be arranged*

Wedding Cakes Baked In-House: *No*

In-House Florist: *Yes*

Overnight Accommodations: *14 suites*

Hotel Discount for Guests of Event: *No*

Complimentary Hospitality Rooms: *No*

Ventana Inn & Spa

The remote, haunting
beauty of Big Sur has served
as inspiration for generations
of artists, lovers, and seekers.
Ventana Inn and Spa, in the
heart of Big Sur, is among the
world's most inspiring places to
stay. Situated on two hundred
forty-three acres, twelve hundred feet above the Pacific
Ocean, the property is known
internationally for its awe-
inspiring vistas, rustic sophis-
tication and romantic allure.

Matthew Millea, execu-
tive chef for Ventana's restaurant, Cielo, which in Spanish
means "heaven," creates rustic
California menus for the
restaurant. The presentations
are simple, with innovative
specials created daily. Lunch
and dinner are served in an
open-beam, raw-cedar dining
room or on the outside terrace
with fifty-mile vistas.
Advance arrangements can
be made to accommodate
groups, special parties, and
weddings.

Ventana Inn and Spa is
renowned as a retreat and
hideaway for celebrities and
others wishing to spend quiet
time in a beautiful setting.

Photo on Page P-20

Highway 1
Big Sur, CA 93920
(831) 667-2331
www.ventanainn.com

OUTDOOR FACILITY ONLY	MAXIMUM SEATING	MAXIMUM M STANDING
Terrace	50	n/a

Exclusive Use of Outdoor Facility: *Yes*

Meeting Rooms: *1 room that seats 8*

Availability of All Facilities: *Year-round*

Reserve for Events: *4 months in advance*

Reserve for Meetings: *1 month*

Cocktail Parties: *Allowed with a negotiable minimum expenditure per person*

Banquet Menu Prices Per Person (food only): *$75-$125* Hors d'oeuvres $15-$30

Buffet Menu Prices Per Person (food only): *Negotiable*

Room Rental Fee/Deposits: *There is a site fee. A deposit is required.*

Cancellation Policy: *Deposit is nonrefundable*

Credit Cards: *AMX, Visa, M/C, Dis*

Parking: *Lot*

Full-Service Bar: *Yes*

Corkage Fee: *n/a*

Dance Floor: *No*

Wheelchair Accessible: *Yes*

Smoking Allowed: *Restricted*

Live Music: *Restricted*

Amplified Music: *No*

Event Coordination Services: *Limited*

Wedding Ceremony Allowed On-Site: *Yes*

Meeting Room Equipment: *None*

Sound System: *No*

Elevated Stage: *No*

Audio Visual: *No*

Restaurant Services: *Yes*

Catering Provided: *Yes*

HYO Caterer: *No*

Kitchen Facilities: *No*

Linens, Silver, Glasses, etc. Provided: *Yes*

Tables and Chairs Provided: *Yes*

Wedding Cakes Baked In-House: *Yes*

In-House Florist: *No*

Overnight Accommodations: *62 guest rooms*

Hotel Discount for Guests of Event: *No*

Complimentary Hospitality Rooms: *No*

UNIQUE LOCATIONS

*S*etting and service have made The Wedding at Pebble Beach an enduring tradition. With imagination and great attention to detail, their catering staff arranges everything to suit your individual needs. From ceremony to reception, your wedding day will be a unique and elegant experience to last a lifetime.

The beautiful area overlooking the 18th fairway of the legendary Pebble Beach Golf Links and Carmel Bay has been a favorite wedding setting for generations.

Their catering staff is experienced in all aspects of wedding planning and coordination, including making arrangements for clergy, cakes, carriages, entertainment, florals, linens, tents, photographers and videographers, rehearsal dinners, and room accommodations. Their desire is to make your special day memorable.

THE 18TH FAIRWAY AT THE LODGE AT PEBBLE BEACH

1700 17-Mile Drive
Pebble Beach, CA 93953
(831) 624-3811
www.pebblebeach.com

AREA AVAILABLE	MAXIMUM SEATING	MAXIMUM STANDING
18th Fairway	250	250

Meeting Rooms: *Yes, at The Lodge at Pebble Beach*

Availability of All Facilities: *Year-round. 18th Fairway used only in conjunction with wedding reception.*

Reserve for Events: *12 months in advance*

Reserve for Meetings: *n/a*

Cocktail Parties: *Cocktail reception following wedding ceremonies only*

Banquet Menu Prices Per Person (food only): *Upon request*

Buffet Menu Prices Per Person (food only): *n/a*

Lawn Usage Fee/Deposits: *The lawn usage fee is $2,000. The deposit is $2,000.*

Cancellation Policy: *Deposit is nonrefundable*

Credit Cards: *All major credit cards*

Parking: *Lot, Valet*

Full-Service Bar: *Yes*

Corkage Fee: *n/a*

Dance Floor: *n/a*

Wheelchair Accessible: *Yes*

Smoking Allowed: *Yes*

Live Music: *Yes*

Amplified Music: *Yes, limited*

Event Coordination Services: *Yes*

Wedding Ceremony Allowed On-Site: *Yes*

Meeting Room Equipment: *All*

Sound System: *Yes*

Elevated Stage: *No*

Audio Visual: *Yes*

Restaurant Services: *Yes*

Catering Provided: *Yes*

HYO Caterer: *No*

Kitchen Facilities: *No*

Linens, Silver, Glasses, etc. Provided: *Yes*

Tables and Chairs Provided: *Yes, chairs at a nominal fee*

Wedding Cakes Baked In-House: *Yes*

In-House Florist: *Yes*

A TASTE OF MONTEREY-WINE TASTING (

A Taste of Monterey is the Monterey County Wine Visitor's Center, which showcases thirty-five wineries and over one hundred different wines. The tasting room is located in an original cannery building that was built in 1918. It is located in the heart of historic Cannery Row, only one block from the Monterey Bay Aquarium and walking distance from the Monterey Plaza Hotel.

Inside this 4,000- square-foot facility are several wine-making exhibits, viticultural displays, murals and a twenty-five-seat theater.

There is an impressive tasting bar and seating area that boasts Monterey's most beautiful and scenic view of the bay. Whether you are planning a wine-tasting reception, a roaming dinner, or a formal plated dinner, your guests are sure to enjoy the peaceful and tranquil atmosphere of this unique location while discovering the world-class wines of Monterey County.

700 Cannery Row
Monterey, CA 93940
(888) 646-5446
www.tastemonterey.com

ROOMS AVAILABLE	MAXIMUM SEATING	MAXIMUM STANDING
Banquet Room	80	180
Outdoor Facilities	n/a	n/a

Exclusive Use of Entire Facility: *Available*

Meeting Rooms: *None*

Availability of All Facilities: *Year-round (evening is preferred)*

Reserve for Events: *As soon as possible*

Reserve for Meetings: *n/a*

Cocktail Parties: *Allowed (wine parties)*

Banquet and Buffet Menu: *n/a*

Room Rental Fee/Deposits: *The room rental fee is a minimum of $400. The deposit is $250.*

Cancellation Policy: *Negotiable*

Credit Cards: *AMX, Visa, M/C, Diners*

Parking: *Lot, Street*

Full-Service Bar: *No, wine and beer only*

Corkage Fee: *n/a*

Dance Floor: *No*

Wheelchair Accessible: *Yes*

Smoking Allowed: *No*

Live Music: *Yes*

Amplified Music: *Yes*

Event Coordination Services: *Yes*

Wedding Ceremony Allowed On-Site: *No*

Meeting Room Equipment: *None*

Sound System: *CD, Video*

Elevated Stage: *No*

Audio Visual: *Yes*

Restaurant Services: *No*

Catering Provided: *Yes*

HYO Caterer: *Yes*

Kitchen Facilities: *Limited*

Linens, Silver, Glasses, etc. Provided: *Wineglasses only*

Tables and Chairs Provided: *Limited*

Wedding Cakes Baked In-House: *No*

In-House Florist: *No*

Balesteri Unlimited Catering

*W*inner of the "Business of Excellence Award 2000." Monterey's best kept secret. Nestled in the foothills, between Del Monte Shopping Center and Skyline Forest. The dining room is spacious, with a spectacular ocean view and space for up to two hundred fifty guests. Lots of beautiful chandeliers highlight the dining room, which features a cozy fireplace, large oak dance floor, and a trellis above with white lights to capture that special moment of your first dance.

Chefs prepare your food with only the freshest ingredients available—choice-grade meats, and fresh poultry and fish. The menus are priced to fit everyone's tastes and budget, from a black-tie event to a casual barbeque, and designed for your creative tastes.

Balesteri provides all your setup, including glassware, china, and linens, and do all the cleanup. All you do is provide the guests!

They work closely with you to ensure that every need is catered to.

150 Mar Vista Drive
Monterey, CA 93940
(831) 655-3700 or 633-0446
www.balestericatering.com

ROOMS AVAILABLE	MAXIMUM SEATING	MAXIMUM STANDING
Dining Room	250	250

Exclusive Use of Entire Facility: *Yes, Dining Room*

Meeting Rooms: *1 meeting room that seats 250 guests*

Availability of All Facilities: *Year-round*

Reserve for Events: *Call for availability*

Reserve for Meetings: *Call for availability*

Cocktail Parties: *Allowed with a minimum of $15 per person (food only)*

Banquet Menu Prices Per Person (food only): *Dinners $21.95-$29.95, Hors d'oeuvres $15.00 minimum*

Buffet Menu Prices Per Person (food only): *Dinners $18.95-$28.95, Hors d'oeuvres $15.00 minimum*

Room Rental Fee/Deposits: *The room rental fee is $500. The deposit to reserve a date is $700.*

Cancellation Policy: *Deposit is nonrefundable*

Credit Cards: *n/a*

Parking: *Lot*

Full-Service Bar: *Yes*

Corkage Fee: Yes, *call for price*

Dance Floor: *Yes*

Wheelchair Accessible: *Yes*

Smoking Allowed: *No*

Live Music: *Yes*

Amplified Music: *Yes*

Event Coordination Services: *Yes*

Wedding Ceremony Allowed On-Site: *Yes*

Meeting Room Equipment: *No*

Sound System: *No*

Elevated Stage: *Yes*

Audio Visual: *No*

Restaurant Services: *Yes*

Catering Provided: *Yes*

HYO Caterer: *No*

Kitchen Facilities: *Yes*

Linen, Silver, Glasses, etc. Provided: *Yes*

Tables and Chairs Provided: *Yes*

Wedding Cakes Baked In-House: *Call for referrals*

In-House Florist: *Call for referrals*

BAYONET/BLACK HORSE GOLF COURSE

Traveling along scenic Highway One, just minutes north of Monterey, you will find the beautiful Bayonet/Black Horse Golf Courses. Their two championship courses not only offer a challenging round of golf to players of all abilities, but also provide a banquet facility overlooking the majestic Monterey Bay. Within this facility you will find a relaxed, quiet atmosphere that will add a special touch to any event.

Bayonet/Black Horse is the ideal setting for weddings, rehearsal dinners, receptions, luncheons and more. The accommodations are composed of an outdoor terrace, a private banquet room, and a main dining room, all with spectacular views of the bay.

From elaborate buffets to a multiple-course prix-fixe menu, the chefs take great pride in the selection of unique menus to accommodate your needs.

Bayonet/Black Horse Golf Courses invite you to visit our facility and experience the unparalleled beauty of the Monterey Bay. Please contact the food and beverage manager for additional information.

1 McClure Way
Seaside, CA 93955
(831) 899-7271 ext. 204
www.bayonetblackhorse.com

ROOMS AVAILABLE	MAXIMUM SEATING	MAXIMUM STANDING
Main Dining Room	200	250
Bayview Room	120	150

Exclusive Use of Indoor and Outdoor Facilities: *Yes*

Meeting Rooms: *1 banquet room that seats up to 100 guests*

Availability of All Facilities: *Year-round*

Reserve for Events: *2 months in advance*

Reserve for Meetings: *2 months in advance*

Cocktail Parties: *Yes*

Banquet Menu Prices Per Person (food only): *Luncheons $8.95-$21.95, Dinners $10.95-$39.95, Hors d'oeuvres $8-$12*

Buffet Menu Prices Per Person (food only): *Luncheons $8.95-$19.95*

Room Rental Fee/Deposits: *The room rental fee is $250 for four hours. The deposit to reserve a date is $250.*

Cancellation Policy: *Deposit is refundable 30 days prior to scheduled event*

Credit Cards: *AMX, Visa, M/C*

Parking: *Lot*

Full-Service Bar: *Yes*

Corkage Fee: *$15*

Dance Floor: *Yes*

Wheelchair Accessible: *Yes*

Smoking Allowed: *Outside only*

Live Music: *Yes*

Amplified Music: *Yes*

Event Coordination Services: *Yes*

Wedding Ceremony Allowed On-Site: *Yes*

Meeting Room Equipment: *Yes*

Sound System: *Yes*

Elevated Stage: *No*

Audio Visual: *Yes*

Restaurant Services: *Yes*

Catering Provided: *Yes*

HYO Caterer: *No*

Kitchen Facilities: *Yes*

Linen, Silver, Glasses, etc. Provided: *Yes*

Tables and Chairs Provided: *Yes*

Wedding Cakes Baked In-House: *No*

In-House Florist: *No*

THE BEACH AND TENNIS CLUB

A short walk from the famous Lodge at Pebble Beach—on the shores of Stillwater Cove—stands a fantastic facility offering superb group opportunities. The Beach and Tennis Club offers two attractive function rooms. The stunning Beach Club Dining Room boasts a glass conservatory and a skylight, creating a dining room full of luxurious sunlight and unobstructed views of Stillwater Cove and the renowned 17th fairway of Pebble Beach Golf Links. This delightful restaurant serves luncheon to members and guests of Pebble Beach Resort's three Inns and is available for private dinners and receptions of up to two hundred fifty-five guests. In addition, the intimate fireside Club Room provides meeting or lunch space for up to fifty guests. The Beach and Tennis Club is an integral complement to the group attractions of The Lodge at Pebble Beach and The Inn at Spanish Bay.

Cypress Drive
P.O. Box 1127
Pebble Beach, CA 93953
(831) 625-8507

ROOMS AVAILABLE	MAXIMUM SEATING	MAXIMUM STANDING
Dining Room	255	255

Exclusive Use of Entire Facility: *From 6 p.m. to 11 p.m.*

Meeting Rooms: *None*

Availability of All Facilities: *Year-round*

Reserve for Events: *12 months in advance*

Reserve for Meetings: *n/a*

Cocktail Parties: *n/a*

Banquet and Buffet Menu Prices Per Person (food only): *Dinners $70-$100, Hors d'oeuvres $25-$45*

Room Rental Fee/Deposits: *The room rental fee is $5,000. The deposit is the room rental fee.*

Cancellation Policy: *Deposit is nonrefundable*

Credit Cards: *AMX, Visa, M/C, Dis*

Parking: *Lot, Street, Valet*

Full-Service Bar: *Yes*

Corkage Fee: *n/a*

Dance Floor: *Yes*

Wheelchair Accessible: *Yes*

Smoking Allowed: *No*

Live Music: *Yes*

Amplified Music: *Yes*

Event Coordination Services: *Yes*

Wedding Ceremony Allowed On-Site: *No*

Meeting Room Equipment: *All*

Sound System: *Yes*

Elevated Stage: *Yes*

Audio Visual: *Yes*

Restaurant Services: *Yes*

Catering Provided: *Yes*

HYO Caterer: *No*

Kitchen Facilities: *No*

Linen, Silver, Glasses, etc. Provided: *Yes*

Tables and Chairs Provided: *Yes*

Wedding Cakes Baked In-House: *Yes*

In-House Florist: *Yes*

CHARDONNAY SAILING CHARTERS

*C*ome aboard the
Chardonnay II and view the
picturesque California coastline as you skim the waters
of one of the world's most
beautiful bays. You'll enjoy
the exhilaration of sailing as
you observe sea otters at play
in the kelp beds. You may see
pelicans with gawky wings
gracefully folded, stream-
lining their headlong dives
to capture dinner.

Experience California's
gorgeous coastline from the
water. You'll see sandy
beaches, cave-studded sand-
stone cliffs, and rocky prom-
ontories dotted with basking
sea lions. Relax on deck or in
the spacious cabin. The large,
modern galley and dining
area provide convenience for
snacks, meals, meetings, and
parties.

P.O. Box 66966
Scotts Valley, CA 95067-6966
(831) 423-1213
www.chardonnay.com

ROOMS AVAILABLE	MAXIMUM SEATING	MAXIMUM STANDING
Chardonnay II Yacht	n/a	49

Exclusive Use of Entire Facility: *Available for a minimum expenditure of $1,260*

Meeting Rooms: *None*

Availability of All Facilities: *Year-round*

Reserve for Events: *As soon as possible*

Cocktail Parties: *Allowed*

Banquet and Buffet Menu: *n/a, prices vary for hors d'oeuvres and beverages*

Room Rental Fee/Deposits: *A 50% deposit is required to confirm reservations*

Cancellation Policy: *Cancellation policy is negotiable*

Credit Cards: *AMX, Visa, M/C*

Parking: *Lot*

Full-Service Bar: *n/a*

Corkage Fee: *n/a*

Dance Floor: *No*

Wheelchair Accessible: *No*

Smoking Allowed: *No*

Live Music: *No*

Amplified Music: *Yes*

Event Coordination Services: *Yes*

Wedding Ceremony Allowed On-Site: *Yes*

Meeting Room Equipment: *No*

Sound System: *Stereo, CD player*

elevated Stage: *Rentable*

Audio Visual: *Rentable*

Restaurant Services: *No*

Catering Provided: *Yes*

HYO Caterer: *Yes*

Kitchen Facilities: *Yes*

Linen, Silver, Glasses, etc. Provided: *Limited*

Tables and Chairs Provided: *Limited*

CHATEAU JULIEN WINE ESTATE

Chateau Julien Wine Estate is located in the rustic hillsides of Carmel Valley. The magnificent setting is an ideal location for any special event.

A private upstairs dining room accommodates up to thirty people. Featuring a twelve-foot antique French table under an open-beamed ceiling, this room is perfect for a candlelight dinner next to the hearth or for beginning an evening with wine and hors d'oeuvres.

The Great Hall, with its high cathedral ceiling, beautiful stained-glass windows, and stone fireplace is a special room that is ideal for elegant dinners seating up to sixty guests.

With a view of the surrounding hillsides, the Cobblestone Garden accommodates up to four hundred people for a memorable themed event or a simple dinner under the stars.

Whether you choose a gourmet dinner in the Great Hall or a celebration in the Chai, the staff will assist you with planning the perfect event to meet your needs.

8940 Carmel Valley Road
Carmel, CA 93923
(831) 624-2600
www.chateaujulien.com

ROOMS AVAILABLE	MAXIMUM SEATING	MAXIMUM STANDING
Great Hall	60	80
Conservatory	90	120
Chai	225	325
Cobblestone Courtyard	400	n/a

Exclusive Use of Entire Facility: *Available*

Meeting Rooms: *None*

Availability of All Facilities: *Year-round*

Reserve for Events: *As soon as possible*

Reserve for Meetings: *n/a*

Cocktail Parties: *Not allowed*

Banquet Menu Prices Per Person (food only): *Luncheons $10-$40, Dinners $40-$150, Hors d'oeuvres $8-$12*

Buffet Menu Prices Per Person (food only): *Luncheons $10-$40, Dinners $30-$70, Hors d'oeuvres $8-$12*

Room Rental Fee/Deposits: *The room rental fee begins at $1,200. The deposit is 10% of entire expenditure.*

Cancellation Policy: *Deposit is nonrefundable*

Credit Cards: *AMX, Visa, M/C*

Parking: *Lot, Street*

Full-Service Bar: *No*

Corkage Fee: *n/a*

Dance Floor: *Rentable*

Wheelchair Accessible: *Yes*

Smoking Allowed: *Yes, outside*

Live Music: *Yes*

Amplified Music: *Yes*

Event Coordination Services: *Yes*

Wedding Ceremony Allowed On-Site: *Yes*

Meeting Room Equipment: *No*

Sound System: *Rentable*

Elevated Stage: *Rentable*

Audio Visual: *Rentable*

Restaurant Services: *No*

Catering Provided: *Yes*

HYO Caterer: *No*

Kitchen Facilities: *Yes*

Linen, Silver, Glasses, etc. Provided: *Yes*

Tables and Chairs Provided: *Yes*

Wedding Cakes Baked In-House: *No*

In-House Florist: *No*

CYPRESS INN

C̲ypress Inn was built in 1929 and is centrally located in Carmel-by-the-Sea. The harmonious restoration of this classic Spanish Mediterranean hotel creates a unique atmosphere in this serene coastal environment.

Each room has a distinctive character with special touches added to create a perfect ambience. The Inn's amenities include private baths, telephones, televisions, daily newspapers, and a decanter of sherry. A variety of deluxe rooms feature wet bars, sitting areas, ocean views, and fireplaces.

The library lounge offers a complimentary continental breakfast, afternoon tea, and a full bar. Relax in the garden courtyard or sit by the fire in the spacious and inviting living room.

Doris Day and partners welcome pets, and the staff provides personalized service found only in small hotels. Wedding ceremonies, receptions and special events can be coordinated by the Cypress Inn.

Lincoln and 7th
P.O. Box 4
Carmel, CA 93921
(831) 624-3871
www.cypress-inn.com

ROOMS AVAILABLE	MAXIMUM SEATING	MAXIMUM STANDING
Courtyard	30	30

Meeting Rooms: *None*

Availability of All Facilities: *Year-round*

Reserve for Events: *As soon as possible*

Reserve for Meetings: *n/a*

Cocktail Parties: *No*

Banquet and Buffet Menu: *n/a*

Room Rental Fee/Deposits: *Site rental fee ranges from $175 to $300*

Cancellation Policy: *Deposit is refundable with 30 days' cancellation notice*

Credit Cards: *AMX, Visa, M/C, Dis*

Parking: *Lot, Street*

Full-Service Bar: *Yes*

Corkage Fee: *$12*

Dance Floor: *No*

Wheelchair Accessible: *Yes*

Smoking Allowed: *No*

Live Music: *Yes, limited*

Amplified Music: *No*

Event Coordination Services: *Yes, limited*

Wedding Ceremony Allowed On-Site: *Yes*

Meeting Room Equipment: *n/a*

Sound System: *No*

Elevated Stage: *No*

Audio Visual: *No*

Restaurant Services: *No*

Catering Provided: *No*

HYO Caterer: *Yes*

Kitchen Facilities: *No*

Linens, Silver, Glasses, etc. Provided: *No*

Tables and Chairs Provided: *No*

Wedding Cake Baked In-House: *No*

In-House Florist: *No*

DEL MONTE PAVILION

Think of the Del Monte Pavilion for your next special event. Your guests relax and celebrate under a heated open- air pavillion adjacent to the ageless beauty of historic Del Monte Golf Course. Events such as barbeques, picnics, receptions, awards ceremonies, and corporate outings are beautifully catered by Pebble Beach chefs.

1300 Sylvan Road
Monterey, CA 93940
(831) 373-2700

ROOMS AVAILABLE	MAXIMUM SEATING	MAXIMUM STANDING
Pavilion Outdoor Facility	150	200

Exclusive Use of Entire Facility: *Available*

Meeting Rooms: *None*

Availability of All Facilities: *Year-round*

Reserve for Events: *As soon as possible*

Reserve for Meetings: *n/a*

Cocktail Parties: *No*

Banquet Menu Prices Per Person (food only): *Luncheons $12.50-$30, Dinners $20-$35, Hors d'oeuvres from $5*

Buffet Menu Prices Per Person (food only): *Luncheons $12-$30, Dinners $15-$30, Hors d'oeuvres from $5*

Room Rental Fee/Deposits: *The room rental fee is negotiable. The deposit to reserve a date is negotiable.*

Cancellation Policy: *Deposit is refundable with 21 days' cancellation notice*

Credit Cards: *AMX, Visa, M/C*

Parking: *Lot*

Full-Service Bar: *Yes*

Corkage Fee: *$15*

Dance Floor: *Yes*

Wheelchair Accessible: *Yes*

Smoking Allowed: *Yes*

Live Music: *Yes*

Amplified Music: *Yes*

Event Coordination Services: *Yes*

Wedding Ceremony Allowed On-Site: *Yes*

Meeting Room Equipment: *No*

Sound System: *No*

Elevated Stage: *No*

Audio Visual: *No*

Restaurant Services: *Yes*

Catering Provided: *Yes*

HYO Caterer: *No*

Kitchen Facilities: *No*

Linen, Silver, Glasses, etc. Provided: *Yes*

Tables and Chairs Provided: *Yes*

Wedding Cakes Baked In-House: *No*

In-House Florist: *No*

GALANTE VINEYARDS

Come experience the rustic elegance of Galante Vineyards, a seven-hundred-acre property nestled in the hills of sunny Carmel Valley. Galante Vineyards focuses on customer service and strives to create a unique personalized event. The outdoor facility is well suited for group gatherings, special theme events, company parties, weddings, wine tastings, tours, and other celebrations for as few as twenty to as many as two thousand people!

Galante offers several private areas for your special event, all overlooking the beautiful and peaceful Cachagua Valley and only ten miles from Carmel Valley. Galante Vineyards makes only ultra-premium estate-bottled wines, specializing in Cabernet Sauvignon, Merlot, and Sauvignon Blanc. With twelve thousand rosebushes beautifying the property, Galante's grounds are truly spectacular. Their wine and roses complement any special event or occasion.

18181 Cachagua Road
Carmel Valley, CA 93924
(800) GALANTE
www. galantevineyards.com

ROOMS AVAILABLE	MAXIMUM SEATING	MAXIMUM STANDING
Barrel Room	20	50
Various Locations	500	2,000

Exclusive Use of Entire Facility: *Available*

Meeting Rooms: *Tent*

Availability of All Facilities: *Year-round*

Reserve for Events: *As soon as possible*

Cocktail Parties: *Yes, beer and wine only*

Banquet and Buffet Menu: *Yes*

Room Rental Fee/Deposits: *The site fee $1,500 Monday-Thursday, $2,000 Friday-Sunday. The deposit is $500 to reserve a date.*

Cancellation Policy: *Deposit is refundable with 90 days' cancellation notice*

Credit Cards: *Visa, M/C*

Parking: *On-site*

Full-Service Bar: *No*

Corkage Fee: *$10, Champagne only*

Dance Floor: *Available upon request*

Wheelchair Accessible: *Yes*

Smoking Allowed: *Specified areas*

Live Music: *Yes*

Amplified Music: *Yes*

Event Coordination Services: *Yes*

Wedding Ceremony Allowed On-Site: *Yes*

Meeting Room Equipment: *None*

Sound System: *Yes*

Elevated Stage: *Yes*

Audio Visual: *No*

Restaurant Services: *No*

Catering Provided: *Yes*

HYO Caterer: *Yes*

Kitchen Facilities: *None*

Linens, Silver, Glasses, etc. Provided: *Available upon request*

Tables and Chairs Provided: *Yes*

Wedding Cakes Baked In-House: *No*

In-House Florist: *Yes*

HAHN ESTATES, SMITH & HOOK WINERY

Along the ridgeline of the Santa Lucia Highlands appellations is the home of Hahn Estates, Smith & Hook Winery. This Hahn family-owned property is located over 1000 feet above the valley floor. The Tasting Room and public decks of the estate afford spectacular views of vines cascading down the mountainside. The vineyards here fashion impeccable wines, with the Cabernets and Merlots historically being among the best in the state. The Tasting Room boasts one of the most interesting and best-stocked winery gift shops in the area. The Tasting Room is open daily 11 to 4 and tours are by appointment.

Nestled on the same property is an old ranch house built in the early 1900s that can comfortably accommodate twenty to twenty-five people for sit-down dinners, bridal showers, family reunions, or business meetings. The outdoor facilities feature a lawn area under oak trees that will accommodate up to two hundred guests. The vineyard views make any occasion memorable.

37700 Foothill Road
Soledad, CA 93960
(831) 678-2132
www.hahnestates.com

ROOMS AVAILABLE	MAXIMUM SEATING	MAXIMUM STANDING
Private Dining Room	25	40
Outdoor Facilities	200	250

Exclusive Use of Indoor Facilities: *Available*

Meeting Rooms: *No*

Availability of All Facilities: *Year-round*

Reserve for Events: *Call for availability*

Reserve for Meetings: *Call for availability*

Cocktail Parties: *No*

Banquet Menu Prices Per Person (food only): *n/a*

Buffet Menu Prices Per Person (food only): *n/a*

Room Rental Fee/Deposits: *The room rental fee is $150-$750*

Cancellation Policy: *n/a*

Credit Cards: *AMX, Visa, M/C, Dis*

Parking: *Lot*

Full-Service Bar: *No*

Corkage Fee: *n/a*

Dance Floor: *Yes, area*

Wheelchair Accessible: *Yes*

Smoking Allowed: *Outside only*

Live Music: *Yes*

Amplified Music: *Yes*

Event Coordination Services: *No*

Wedding Ceremony Allowed On-Site: *Yes*

Meeting Room Equipment: *No*

Sound System: *No*

Elevated Stage: *No*

Audio Visual: *No*

Restaurant Services: *No*

Catering Provided: *No*

HYO Caterer: *Yes*

Kitchen Facilities: *Yes*

Linen, Silver, Glasses, etc. Provided: *No*

THE HOLLY FARM

A wedding at The Holly Farm is a celebration of love as well as a reunion of your closest friends and family. The Farm was exclusively designed and is maintained and operated as a wedding destination facility. The five night, six-day package has been described as a "Wedding Moon." The Holly Farm takes care of the mandatory details, freeing you to spend your time relaxing, settling in, and enjoying your wedding celebration.

The Holly Farm is an old historic hacienda located in sunny Carmel Valley. Lush tropical floral gardens surround the stone waterfall pond, courtyard fountains, and the Carriage House activity barn on this five-acre private estate. The early California-style adobe home accommodates ten to twelve guests with its four bedrooms and three baths. Framed by redwood decking, the Banana Cabaña, a rustic redwood bungalow, houses six to eight people. The Holly Farm package also includes the Windmill Suite Honeymoon Cottage.

A five-night, six-day inclusive wedding at The Holly Farm is the same price as most four-hour hotel receptions.

Photo on Page P-7

9200 Carmel Valley Road
Carmel, CA 93923
(831) 625-1926
www.hollyfarm.com

ROOMS AVAILABLE	MAXIMUM SEATING	MAXIMUM STANDING
Carriage House	100	250
Lawn Umbrella Seating	250	250
Exclusive Use of Indoor and Outdoor Facilities	250	250

Exclusive Use of Indoor and Outdoor Facilities: *Yes*

Meeting Rooms: *1 meeting room that seats 100 guests*

Availability of All Facilities: *Year-round*

Reserve for Events: *6-8 months in advance*

Reserve for Meetings: *2 months in advance*

Cocktail Parties: *Arrangements to be made based upon your specific needs*

Banquet Menu Prices Per Person (food only): *n/a*

Buffet Menu Prices Per Person (food only): *Luncheons and Dinners start at $40. Private consultation with The Holly Farm chef included in rental.*

Room Rental Fee/Deposits: *Site fee is $25,000 for 5 nights and 6 days, all inclusive. Deposit to reserve a date is $5,000.*

Cancellation Policy: *Deposit is refundable if date can be re-booked*

Credit Cards: *No, cashiers checks only*

Parking: *Lot on site with parking assistants*

Full-Service Bar: *No*

Corkage Fee: *None*

Dance Floor: *Yes*

Wheelchair Accessible: *Yes*

Smoking Allowed: *Outside*

Live Music: *Yes*

Amplified Music: *Yes*

Event Coordination Services: *Yes*

Wedding Ceremony Allowed On-Site: *Yes*

Meeting Room Equipment: *No*

Sound System: *Yes*

Elevated Stage: *No*

Audio Visual: *No*

Restaurant Services: *No*

Catering Provided: *Yes*

HYO Caterer: *No*

Kitchen Facilities: *No*

Linen, Silver, Glasses, etc. Provided: *Yes*

Tables and Chairs Provided: *Yes*

Wedding Cakes Baked In-House: *No*

In-House Florist: *Yes*

Overnight Accommodations: *Sleeps 22*

Hotel Discount for Guests of Event: *No*

Complimentary Hospitality Rooms: *Yes*

THE HOLMAN RANCH

*B*uilt in 1928 as a gentleman's country retreat, the four-hundred-acre Holman Ranch was converted to a guest ranch in the 1940s by Mr. and Mrs. C.E. Holman, well-known Monterey Peninsula civic leaders. It quickly became the center of Carmel Valley social life as well as a hideaway for many Hollywood celebrities.

Known as a miniature San Simeon, The Holman Ranch was originally built using stone and oak from the property grounds. This Spanish-style hacienda became known throughout the area for its open-beamed ceilings, unique craftsmanship, and panoramic view of Carmel Valley.

Today the ranch has been refurbished and the grounds and buildings returned to their original, classic state, providing a remarkable setting for weddings, parties, meetings, or commercial applications. The site fee includes the use of the Lounge, Theater, Courtyard, Library, Game Room, Garden Patio, and Charlie Chaplin Room. The pool, wine cellar, and rodeo arena are also available.

Holman Road
Carmel Valley, CA 93924
(831) 659-2640
www.holmanranch.com

ROOMS AVAILABLE	MAXIMUM SEATING	MAXIMUM STANDING
Theater Banquet Room	60	90
Rose Patio and Lawn	200	250
The Carriage House	150	200
Exclusive Use of Outdoor Facilities	350	500

Exclusive Use of Indoor and Outdoor Facilities: *Site fee is $3,500 and up*

Meeting Rooms: *2 meeting rooms that seat 150 guests, theater style*

Availability of All Facilities: *Mid-February to mid-November. Hours by arrangement.*

Reserve for Events: *12 months in advance*

Reserve for Meetings: *3 months in advance*

Cocktail Parties: *Allowed. Bring your own bar.*

Banquet Menu: *n/a*

Buffet Menu: *n/a*

Rental Fee/Deposits: *The site fee for under 50 guests is $3,500 Sunday-Friday, $4,500 Saturday. For 50 to 200 guests the site fee is $4,000 Sunday-Friday, $5,000 Saturday. The site fee for over 200 guests and for nonprofit groups is negotiable. The fees for additional areas such as the pool, wine cellar, and rodeo arena are negotiable. The deposit to reserve a date is $2,000. Rates subject to change.*

Cancellation Policy: *Advance deposits are nonrefundable*
Credit Cards: *AMX, Visa, M/C*
Parking: *Available along driveway up to estate*
Full-Service Bar: *Allowed*
Corkage Fee: *n/a*
Dance Floor: *Yes, area*
Wheelchair Accessible: *Yes*
Smoking Allowed: *Outdoor Areas*
Live Music: *Yes, with restrictions*
Amplified Music: *Yes, with limitations*
Event Coordination Services: *No*
Wedding Ceremony Allowed On-Site: *Yes*
Meeting Room Equipment: *VCR with overhead screen*
Sound System: *Speakers, VCR, and CD in Theater only*
Elevated Stage: *Yes*
Audio Visual: *Yes*
Restaurant Services: *No*
Catering Provided: *No*
HYO Caterer: *Yes*
Kitchen Facilities: *Yes, limited*
Linen, Silver, Glasses, etc. Provided: *No*
Tables and Chairs Provided: *Yes, redwood furniture only*
Wedding Cakes Baked In-House: *No*
In-House Florist: *No*

JOHN GARDINER'S TENNIS RANCH

*W*rapped in beautiful botanical gardens with spacious accommodations and world-famous cuisine, John Gardiner's Tennis Ranch in sunny Carmel Valley is designed to welcome guests in an atmosphere of comfort and relaxation.

Offering a private and secluded setting with a full-size heated swimming pool, jacuzzi, and saunas, elegant dining rooms and poolside patio, fitness center, massage rooms, and outstanding gourmet cuisine.

Enjoy breakfast in the glass-roofed garden room or buffet-style lunch on the sunny poolside patio. Gather with friends by the fire for cocktails and hors d'oeuvres, followed by a sumptuous five-course dinner. The menu features such delicacies as duet of prawns, Chilean sea bass, seared duck breast, and rack of lamb.

114 Carmel Valley Rd.
Carmel, CA 93924
(831) 659-2207
www.tennis-ranch.com

ROOMS AVAILABLE	MAXIMUM SEATING	MAXIMUM STANDING	MAXIMUM THEATER
Clubhouse Dining Room (private)	60	100	60
Garden Room	60	100	80
Sun Room	20	50	20
Outdoor Facilities: Clubhouse Patio	125	125	60

Exclusive Use of Indoor Facilities: *Available*

Exclusive Use of Outdoor Facilities: *Available*

Meeting Rooms: *3 meeting rooms*

Availability of All Facilities: *Year-round*

Reserve for Events: *6 months in advance*

Reserve for Meetings: *6 months in advance*

Cocktail Parties Only: *Allowed with a minimum expenditure of $25 per person (excluding tax and tip)*

Banquet Menu Prices Per Person (food only): *Luncheons $25-$45, Dinners $45-$95, Hors d'oeuvres price varies*

Buffet Menu Prices Per Person (food only): *n/a*

Room Rental Fee/Deposits: *The room rental is $200-$2,500. The deposit is $200-$2500.*

Cancellation Policy: *Deposit is refundable with at least 6 months' notice*

Credit Cards: *AMX, Visa, M/C*

Parking: *Valet*

Full-Service Bar: *Yes*

Corkage Fee: *n/a*

Dance Floor: *Can be arranged*

Wheelchair Accessible: *Yes*

Smoking Allowed: *No*

Live Music: *Yes*

Amplified Music: *Yes*

Event Coordination Services: *Yes*

Wedding Ceremony Allowed On-Site: *Yes*

Meeting Room Equipment: *Can be arranged*

Sound System: *Can be arranged*

Elevated Stage: *Can be arranged*

Audio Visual: *Yes*

Restaurant Services: *Yes*

Catering Provided: *Yes*

HYO Caterer: *No*

Kitchen Facilities: *Hotel use only*

Linens, Silver, Glasses, etc. Provided: *Yes*

Tables and Chairs Provided: *Yes*

Wedding Cakes Baked In-House: *No*

In-House Florist: *Yes*

Overnight Accommodations: *17 guest rooms*

Hotel Discount for Guests of Event: *Yes*

Complimentary Hospitality Rooms: *No*

Imagine your event at the Maritime Museum of Monterey, home of the comprehensive and valuable Allen Knight Nautical Collection. This historic landmark, located just off Fisherman's Wharf offers the perfect lighting for your evening once the sun sets on the bay. The Maritime Museum is available for you beginning at 5 p.m. each day of the week and is suitable for a wide range of events from intimate sit-down dinners for up to one hundred twenty-five people to receptions for up to four hundred people. The facility also offers a theater with state-of-the-art audiovisual equipment. The Maritime Museum is a wonderfully unique setting, perfect for your event in historic Monterey.

MARITIME MUSEUM OF MONTEREY

The Stanton Center
5 Custom House Plaza
Monterey, CA 93940
(831) 372-2608 ext. 14

ROOMS AVAILABLE	MAXIMUM SEATING	MAXIMUM STANDING
Museum/Theater/Lobby	125	400
Museum/Lobby	125	400
Theater/Lobby	100	200
Outdoor Facility: Observation Deck	16	40

Exclusive Use of Indoor and Outdoor Facilities: *Available from 5p.m to 10 p.m.*

Meeting Rooms: *2 meeting rooms that can seat from 40 to 100*

Availability of All Facilities: *Year-round after 5 p.m.*

Reserve for Events: *As soon as possible*

Reserve for Meetings: *As soon as possible*

Cocktail Parties: *Yes*

Banquet and Buffet Menu: *n/a*

Room Rental Fee/Deposits: *The base room rental fee ranges from $500 to $1,500, with extra charges for additional people. Deposit to reserve a date is $350.*

Cancellation Policy: *Deposit is refundable with 90 days' cancellation notice.*

Credit Cards: *Visa, M/C*

Parking: *Lot*

Full-Service Bar: *No*

Corkage Fee: *n/a*

Dance Floor: *Yes (in lobby)*

Wheelchair Accessible: *Yes*

Smoking Allowed: *No*

Live Music: *Yes*

Amplified Music: *Yes*

Event Coordination Services: *Limited*

Wedding Ceremony Allowed On-Site: *Yes*

Meeting Room Equipment: *Yes*

Sound System: *Yes*

Elevated Stage: *Yes*

Audio Visual: *Yes, at additional cost*

Restaurant Services: *No*

Catering Provided: *No*

HYO Caterer: *Yes*

Kitchen Facilities: *Yes, at additional cost*

Linens, Silver, Glasses, etc. Provided: *No*

Tables and Chairs Provided: *No*

Wedding Cakes Baked In-House: *No*

In-House Florist: *No*

MONTEREY BAY AQUARIUM

Innovative events demand innovative settings, and the Aquarium's array of habitat galleries and exhibits offers your group just that, with activities and facilities tailored to your needs. Now you can explore the Aquarium in a way few can—by reserving all or part of it exclusively for your private event. Groups from thirty to twenty-five hundred can meet for everything from receptions to banquets to meetings, with limitless options for menus, themes, and entertainment.

Life-size models of whales and dolphins swim overhead in their Marine Mammals Gallery, where exquisite sit-down banquets for up to two hundred people, or receptions for more, take place. The three-story-high Kelp Forest exhibit is a complex living community where fishes weave among swaying kelp fronds. Creative banquets for up to ninety can be staged at the foot of its towering windows.

886 Cannery Row
Monterey, CA 93940
(831) 648-4928
www.mbayaq.org

ROOMS AVAILABLE	MAXIMUM SEATING	MAXIMUM STANDING
Marine Mammals Gallery	200	1,500
Kelp Forest	80	n/a
Outer Bay Wing	104	400
Ocean View Conference Room	40	100
Outdoor Facilities	n/a	n/a

Exclusive Use of Indoor and Outdoor Facilities: *Available*

Meeting Rooms: *1 meeting room that can seat 40 guests*

Availability of All Facilities: *Year-round*

Reserve for Events: *6 months to 1 year in advance*

Reserve for Meetings: *6 months to 1 year in advance*

Cocktail Parties: *Allowed with a negotiable minimum expenditure*

Banquet Menu Prices Per Person (food only): *Call for up-to-date information*

Buffet Menu Prices Per Person (food only): *Call for up-to-date information*

Room Rental Fee/Deposits: *Facility rental fee starts at $2,950 for the first 100 guests Sunday–Thursday, and $3,450 for the first 100 guests, Friday or Saturday. The deposit is based on the number of people in the group.*

Cancellation Policy: *50% of deposit will be refunded with 6 months' cancellation notice. There is no refund with less than 6 months' notice.*

Credit Cards: *None*

Parking: *Street, Valet can be arranged*

Full-Service Bar: *Yes*

Corkage Fee: *$15*

Dance Floor: *Existing floors, can be arranged*

Wheelchair Accessible: *Yes*

Smoking Allowed: *No, outdoors only*

Live Music: *Yes*

Amplified Music: *Yes*

Event Coordination Services: *Yes*

Wedding Ceremony Allowed On-Site: *Yes*

Meeting Room Equipment: *All*

Sound System: *Yes*

Elevated Stage: *Can be arranged*

Audio Visual: *Yes*

Restaurant Services: *Yes*

Catering Provided: *Yes*

HYO Caterer: *No*

Kitchen Facilities: *No*

Linens, Silver, Glasses, etc. Provided: *Yes*

Tables and Chairs Provided: *Yes*

Wedding Cakes Baked In-House: *No*

In-House Florist: *No*

MONTEREY MUSEUM OF ART AT LA MIRADA

La Mirada is one of the region's most significant historic structures, as well as one of the most beautiful, with its lovely landscaped gardens overlooking Lake El Estero. The original adobe portion of the house, built in the early nineteenth century, was the residence of Mexican general Jose Castro until his return to Mexico following the Mexican-American War. In the 1930s, the property passed to the Work family, and in 1983 the estate, including fine antiques and decorative art, was deeded to the Monterey Museum of Art Association by Frank Work.

Visitors to La Mirada are invited to explore early California history, to experience a taste of life on the Peninsula as it was in the 1920s, and to enjoy exhibitions which focus on California regional art, Asian art, and art of the Pacific Rim. La Mirada is available for use only to corporations and organizations.

720 Via Mirada
Monterey, CA 93940
(831) 372-3689

ROOMS AVAILABLE	MAXIMUM SEATING	MAXIMUM STANDING
Museum/Gardens/Courtyard	80	250
Castro-Work Adobe	12	75
Gardens/Courtyard	40-150	150+

Exclusive Use of Outdoor Facility: *Available*

Exclusive Use of Entire Facility: *Available depending upon exhibition schedule*

Meeting Rooms: *One conference room. Capacity varies according to seating arrangement.*

Availability of All Facilities: *Year-round to corporations and organizations only*

Reserve for Events: *As soon as possible*

Reserve for Meetings: *As soon as possible*

Cocktail Parties: *Allowed*

Banquet and Buffet Menu: *n/a*

Room Rental Fee/Deposits: *The room rental fee ranges from $350 to $2,500. The deposit is 50% of the fee.*

Cancellation Policy: *Deposit is refundable with 30 days' cancellation notice*

Credit Cards: *Visa, M/C*

Parking: *Lot (limited)*

Full-Service Bar: *Allowed*

Corkage Fee: *n/a*

Dance Floor: *No*

Wheelchair Accessible: *Yes*

Smoking Allowed: *No*

Live Music: *Restricted*

Amplified Music: *No*

Event Coordination Services: *No*

Wedding Ceremony Allowed On-Site: *No*

Meeting Room Equipment: *None*

Sound System: *No*

Elevated Stage: *No*

Audio Visual: *No*

Restaurant Services: *No*

Catering Provided: *No*

HYO Caterer: *Yes*

Kitchen Facilities: *Very limited*

Linen, Silver, Glasses, etc. Provided: *No*

NATIONAL STEINBECK CENTER

The National Steinbeck Center is a spectacular 37,000-square-foot museum in historic Old Town Salinas and the perfect location for any special event. As well as honoring John Steinbeck's life, work, and values through multisensory exhibits, the National Steinbeck Center is a unique setting for groups of fifty to five hundred for meetings, seminars, receptions, parties, and special events.

Reserve the entire Museum or choose just part of it—ranging from divisible meeting rooms, an enclosed courtyard, a quaint yet elegant cafe, a spacious orientation theatre and permanent exhibits, or the ever-changing art and cultural exhibits. The spectacular glass-enclosed atrium at the Main Street entrance is a perfect spot for greeting guests or for holding a more intimate function.

On-site catering is available for all of your dining necessities, and the staff is always ready to assist you in creating the ideal event for your personal or business needs.

One Main Street
Salinas, CA 93901
(831) 796-3833
www.steinbeck.org

ROOMS AVAILABLE	MAXIMUM SEATING	MAXIMUM STANDING
Salinas Room	215	215
Santa Rita Room	107	107
Alisal Room	107	107
Rotunda	200	250
The Courtyard	n/a	50
Exclusive Use of Entire Facility	n/a	500

Exclusive Use of Entire Facility: *Available*

Meeting Rooms: *2 meeting rooms that each seat up to 107 guests*

Availability of All Facilities: *Year-round*

Reserve for Events: *1 month in advance, except holidays*

Reserve for Meetings: *1 months in advance*

Cocktail Parties: *Allowed after 6 p.m.*

Banquet Menu Prices Per Person (food only): *Luncheons from $15.50, Dinners from $23.50, Hors d'oeuvres from $9.95*

Buffet Menu Prices Per Person (food only): *Luncheons from $15.50, Dinners from $23.50, Hors d'oeuvres from $9.95*

Room Rental Fee/Deposits: *The room rental fee varies. The deposit is $500.*

Cancellation Policy: *Deposit is nonrefundable*

Credit Cards: *AMX, Visa, M/C, Dis*

Parking: *Lot, Street*

Full-Service Bar: *Yes*

Corkage Fee: *$10*

Dance Floor: *Yes*

Wheelchair Accessible: *Yes*

Smoking Allowed: *No*

Live Music: *Yes*

Amplified Music: *Yes*

Event Coordination Services: *Yes*

Wedding Ceremony Allowed On-Site: *Yes*

Meeting Room Equipment: *Yes*

Sound System: *Yes*

Elevated Stage: *Yes*

Audio Visual: *Yes*

Restaurant Services: *Yes*

Catering Provided: *Yes*

HYO Caterer: *No*

Kitchen Facilities: *Yes*

Linen, Silver, Glasses, etc. Provided: *Yes*

Tables and Chairs Provided: *Yes*

Wedding Cakes Baked In-House: *No*

In-House Florist: *No*

OLD WHALING STATION ADOBE AND GARDEN

The Old Whaling Station Adobe and Garden is an historic site operated by the Junior League of Monterey County. They would be delighted to share their beautiful home and flowering gardens with you for a wedding, reception, party, or special event.

Located in Heritage Harbor next door to the First Brick House in California, the Adobe has a non-usable fireplace, a mahogany dining room table, a sunroom, and an arbor in the garden. These elegant and unique surroundings make any function picture perfect. Step into history... leave with a memory.

Heritage Harbor
391 Decatur Street
Monterey, CA 93940
(831) 375-5356

ROOMS AVAILABLE	MAXIMUM SEATING	MAXIMUM STANDING
Adobe	50	50
Adobe & Garden	150	150

Exclusive Use of Entire Facility: *Available*

Meeting Rooms: *4 meeting rooms*

Availability of All Facilities: *Year-round*

Reserve for Events: *As soon as possible*

Reserve for Meetings: *As soon as possible*

Cocktail Parties: *Yes*

Banquet and Buffet Menu: *n/a*

Room Rental Fee/Deposits: *The rental fee ranges from $600 to $900 depending on the day of the week. The deposit to reserve a date is half of the rental fee. A refundable security deposit of $500 is required when the renter receives key/security system instructions.*

Cancellation Policy: *Booking deposit is nonrefundable. Security deposit may be forfeited due to misuse of the building such as damage to the building or failure to clean facility sufficiently.*

Credit Cards: *None*

Parking: *Lot, Street*

Full-Service Bar: *Allowed*

Corkage Fee: *n/a*

Dance Floor: *Yes*

Wheelchair Accessible: *Yes, except upstairs*

Smoking Allowed: *No*

Live Music: *Yes, Garden only*

Amplified Music: *Yes*

Event Coordination Services: *No*

Wedding Ceremony Allowed On-Site: *Yes*

Meeting Room Equipment: *None*

Sound System: *No*

Elevated Stage: *No*

Audio Visual: *No*

Restaurant Services: *No*

Catering Provided: *No*

HYO Caterer: *Yes*

Kitchen Facilities: *Yes*

Linens, Silver, Glasses, etc. Provided: *Yes*

Tables and Chairs Provided: *Yes*

Wedding Cakes Baked In-House: *No*

In-House Florist: *No*

RANCHO CAÑADA GOLF CLUB

After twenty-five years as one of the most popular event destinations on the Monterey Peninsula, Rancho Cañada Golf Club is proud to present a totally new and improved clubhouse with all the amenities of a private country club or fine hotel. Extensive clubhouse renovations significantly increase the space available for wedding receptions, social and business banquets, club luncheons, and group meetings. Design flexibility now accommodates private groups from fifty to one thousand.

The only thing that hasn't changed is the club's reputation for fine food and friendly, professional service. Great care is evident in every detail, from the quality of menu ingredients to the fresh flower arrangements. Rancho Cañada Golf Club offers a unique setting overlooking a beautiful golf course and Carmel Valley vistas. Outdoor as well as indoor facilities are available, and parking is plentiful. When your next memorable event demands perfection, you can rely upon the Rancho Cañada Golf Club staff.

4860 Carmel Valley Road
Carmel, CA 93923
(831) 624-0111
www.carmel-golf.com

ROOMS AVAILABLE	MAXIMUM SEATING	MAXIMUM STANDING
Main Dining Room	130	n/a
Merienda Room	225	300
Fiesta Room	400	650
Boardroom	50	60
Outdoor Facilities	150	150
Exclusive Use of Indoor Facilities	700	1,200

Exclusive Use of Outdoor Facilities: *Available with a minimum guest count of 50*

Exclusive Use of Entire Facility: *Available with a minimum guest count of 600 and a minimum total expenditure of $15,000*

Meeting Rooms: *4 meeting rooms that seat from 40 to 400 guests*

Availability of All Facilities: *Year-round*

Reserve for Events: *As soon as possible*

Reserve for Meetings: *As soon as possible*

Cocktail Parties: *Allowed with a minimum expenditure of $10 per person (excluding tax and tip)*

Banquet Menu Prices Per Person (food only): *Luncheons $12-$18, Dinners $20-$35, Hors d'oeuvres $8-$25*

Buffet Menu Prices Per Person (food only): *Luncheons $12-$20, Dinners $20-$40, Hors d'oeuvres $10-$25*

Room Rental Fee/Deposits: *Room rental fee is negotiable. Deposit amount is $500.*

Cancellation Policy: *Deposit is nonrefundable*

Credit Cards: *AMX, Visa, M/C*

Parking: *Lot*

Full-Service Bar: *Yes*

Corkage Fee: *$9*

Dance Floor: *Yes*

Wheelchair Accessible: *Yes*

Smoking Allowed: *Restricted*

Live Music: *Yes*

Amplified Music: *Yes*

Event Coordination Services: *Yes*

Wedding Ceremony Allowed On-Site: *Yes*

Meeting Room Equipment: *Screen, TV, VCR*

Sound System: *Yes*

Elevated Stage: *Yes*

Audio Visual: *Yes*

Restaurant Services: *Yes*

Catering Provided: *Yes*

HYO Caterer: *No*

Kitchen Facilities: *No*

Linens, Silver, Glasses, etc. Provided: *Yes*

Tables and Chairs Provided: *Yes*

Beaches, Gardens, and Parks Directory

BEACHES

Asilomar State Beach (831) 372-4076
Carmel River State Beach (831) 624-4909
Monastery Beach (831) 624-4909
Carmel Beach (831) 624-3543

*A*silomar State Beach, in Pacific Grove, consists of one long sand beach and many smaller rocky beaches.

Carmel River State Beach is a large sandy beach at the mouth of the Carmel River.

Monastery Beach is adjacent to Carmel River State Beach.

Carmel Beach is a beautiful white-sand beach at the bottom of Ocean Avenue in Carmel.

Parking at all of the beaches is limited, and reservations are not accepted. Small informal ceremonies are recommended.

AREA	MAX. CAPACITY	BBQ/ KITCHEN	TABLES	FEE
Asilomar State Beach	unlimited	no/no	none	none
Carmel River State Beach	unlimited	yes*/no	none	none
Monastery Beach	unlimited	yes*/no	none	none
Carmel Beach	unlimited	yes*/no	none	none

Rest Rooms: *Carmel River State Beach, Monastery Beach, and Carmel Beach*

Outdoor Night Lighting: *No*

Amplified Music: *No*

Security Deposit: *Please call*

Responsible for Cleanup: *You*

Alcohol Allowed: *Please call*

Permit Required: *Please call*

Insurance Required: *Please call*

Gazebo: *No*

Other Amenities: *No*

Reservations: *Beaches cannot be reserved Park Rangers must be notified.*

* *contained*

CARMEL VALLEY COMMUNITY YOUTH CENTER

25 Ford Road
Carmel Valley, CA 93924
(831) 659-3983

AREA	MAX. CAPACITY	BBQ/ KITCHEN	TABLES	FEE
Barbecue Area	300	BBQ pit	8-10	$150
River Rock BBQ Area	300	BBQ pit	8-10	$150
Park Area	unlimited			

Rest Rooms: *Yes*

Outdoor Night Lighting: *No*

Amplified Music: *Yes*

Security Deposit: *Yes*

Responsible for Cleanup: *You*

Alcohol Allowed: *Yes*

Permit Required: *No*

Insurance Required: *Depends on activity*

Gazebo: *Yes*

Other Amenities: *Building with kitchen, folding tables and chairs, public pool, volleyball court, horseshoe pits, outdoor stage, playground*

Reservations: *1 month in advance*

The five-acre Carmel Valley Community Youth Center and Park, ten miles west of Highway One in sunny Carmel Valley Village, provides year-round recreational opportunities for children, families, and the young at heart. The facility features two large barbecue areas, one with a gazebo. The outdoor facility also features an outdoor stage, playground, pool, volleyball court, and horseshoe pits.

COOPER-MOLERA ADOBE GARDEN

Corner of Polk and Alvarado
Monterey, CA 93940
(831) 649-7118

The Cooper-Molera Adobe Garden in Old Monterey is a beautiful, historic area enclosed by an eight-foot wall. Capacity is approximately one hundred fifty people for a sit-down dinner or three hundred for a stand-up reception. Reservations will be accepted by the Monterey State Historic Park up to one year in advance.

AREA	MAX. CAPACITY	BBQ/ KITCHEN	TABLES	FEE
Garden	300	no	no	$500 min.

Rest Rooms: *Yes*

Outdoor Night Lighting: *No*

Amplified Music: *Restricted*

Security Deposit: *Yes*

Responsible for Cleanup: *You*

Alcohol Allowed: *Yes*

Permit Required: *Yes*

Insurance Required: *Yes*

Gazebo: *No*

Other Amenities: *Barn and Skylight Room available for additional fees*

Reservations: *Can be made up to 1 year in advance*

El Estero Park

Del Monte and Camino Aguajito
Monterey, CA 93940
(831) 646-3866

AREA	MAX. CAPACITY	BBQ/ KITCHEN	TABLES	FEE
El Estero Park	200	BBQ	yes	$10-$20

Rest Rooms: *Yes*

Outdoor Night Lighting: *No*

Amplified Music: *No*

Security Deposit: *No*

Responsible for Cleanup: *You*

Alcohol Allowed: *By permit only*

Permit Required: *Yes*

Insurance Required: *No*

Gazebo: *No*

Other Amenities: *Dennis the Menace park, ball field, snack bar, water*

Reservations: *As soon as possible*

𝒫art of a forty-five-acre multiuse recreation area in the center of Monterey, El Estero Park is situated around a lake and Dennis the Menace Park. The reservable picnic area has a two-hundred-person maximum capacity, barbecue, water, and rest rooms. The park is a picnic area and not necessarily suited to weddings.

ELMARIE DYKE OPEN SPACE

Between 16th and 17th above Central
Pacific Grove, CA 93950
(831) 648-5730

*E*lmarie Dyke Open Space
is located adjacent to
Chautauqua Hall. It has
been landscaped as an urban
garden with flowering plants,
a fountain, benches and
tables, and a gazebo. The site
is a popular spot for garden
weddings.

AREA	MAX. CAPACITY	BBQ/ KITCHEN	TABLES	FEE
Elmarie Dyke Open Space	40	no	yes	$100

Rest Rooms: *No*

Outdoor Night Lighting: *Yes*

Amplified Music: *No*

Security Deposit: *No*

Responsible for Cleanup: *You*

Alcohol Allowed: *No*

Permit Required: *Yes*

Insurance Required: *No*

Gazebo: *Yes*

Other Amenities: *Fountain, benches*

Reservations: *Permit serves as reservation*

GEORGE WASHINGTON PARK

Sinex Avenue and Alder Street
Pacific Grove, CA 93950
(831) 648-5730

AREA	MAX. CAPACITY	BBQ/ KITCHEN	TABLES	FEE
Large Picnic Area	200	BBQ	yes	$25-$100

Rest Rooms: *Yes*

Outdoor Night Lighting: *Yes*

Amplified Music: *With council approval*

Security Deposit: *No*

Responsible for Cleanup: *You*

Alcohol Allowed: *No*

Permit Required: *Yes*

Insurance Required: *No*

Gazebo: *No*

Other Amenities: *Play structure, baseball field*

Reservations: *Permit serves as reservation*

George Washington Park is the largest of Pacific Grove's city parks. Most of the park is natural-appearing, unimproved forest land that offers important wildlife habitat, and monarch butterflies reside here annually from October to March. The park also contains picnic tables, barbecue grills, rest rooms, a large play structure, and a baseball field.

JEWELL PARK

Central and Grand
Pacific Grove, CA 93950
(831) 648-5730

*J*ewell Park is a small block park bordered by the city's museum, library, and Chamber of Commerce. The park's urban character is established by a well-maintained lawn area, specimen trees, gentle topography, and a small meeting building with a small gazebo suitable for weddings or outdoor performances.

AREA	MAX. CAPACITY	BBQ/ KITCHEN	TABLES	FEE
Park and Gazebo	100	no	no	$100
Building	20	kitchen	no	$15/hr.

Rest Rooms: *No*

Outdoor Night Lighting: *No*

Amplified Music: *With council approval*

Security Deposit: *No*

Responsible for Cleanup: *You*

Alcohol Allowed: *No*

Permit Required: *Yes*

Insurance Required: *No*

Gazebo: *Yes*

Other Amenities: *Meeting building with kitchen*

Reservations: *Permit serves as reservation*

LAGUNA SECA RECREATION AREA

1025 Monterey/Salinas Highway 68
Salinas, CA 93908
(831) 758-3604

*L*aguna Seca's recreation area is located between the picturesque Monterey Peninsula and the Salinas Valley's "Steinbeck Country" on Highway 68. Home to the world-famous Mazda Raceway Laguna Seca, the Skip Barber Racing School and numerous special events, there is truly something for everyone, including access to miles of Bureau of Land Management trails. Laguna Seca is an excellent location for your next special event.

AREA	MAX. CAPACITY	BBQ/ KITCHEN	TABLES	FEE
Island Group Area	1,000	BBQ pit	yes	$160 min.
Track View Area & Media Center	1,000	BBQ pit	yes	$260

Rest Rooms: *Yes*

Outdoor Night Lighting: *Yes*

Amplified Music: *With permit*

Security Deposit: *$100*

Responsible for Cleanup: *Renter*

Alcohol Allowed: *Yes*

Permit Required: *No*

Insurance Required: *Yes, if elements of event require it*

Gazebo: *No*

Other Amenities: *Rifle and pistol range, campgrounds, biking trails, off-highway vehicle area, RV group building*

Reservations: *Can be made 6 months to 1 year in advance*

Lovers Point Park

Ocean View Boulevard
Pacific Grove, CA 93950
(831) 648-5730

The amenities of Lovers Point Park include a large lawn area, a sand volleyball court, a toddler's swimming pool, sandy beaches, rocky outcrops, a concrete pier structure, a snack bar, and nearby restaurants. Lovers Point is used for picnicking, fishing, sunning, and surfing.

AREA	MAX. CAPACITY	BBQ/ KITCHEN	TABLES	FEE
Lovers Point Park	restricted	BBQ	yes	no

Rest Rooms: *Yes*

Outdoor Night Lighting: *No*

Amplified Music: *No*

Security Deposit: *No*

Responsible for Cleanup: *You*

Alcohol Allowed: *No*

Permit Required: *Yes, for weddings*

Insurance Required: *No*

Gazebo: *No*

Other Amenities: *Volleyball court, snack bar, and BBQ area*

Reservations: *Yes, for weddings and special events*

Memory Garden

Custom House Plaza near Scott & Olivier Sts.
Monterey, CA 93940
(831) 649-7118

AREA	MAX. CAPACITY	BBQ/ KITCHEN	TABLES	FEE
Memory Garden	500	BBQ pit	no	$500 min.

Rest Rooms: *Yes*

Outdoor Night Lighting: *No*

Amplified Music: *Restricted*

Security Deposit: *Yes*

Responsible for Cleanup: *You*

Alcohol Allowed: *Yes*

Permit Required: *Yes*

Insurance Required: *Yes*

Gazebo: *No*

Other Amenities: *No*

Reservations: *Can be made up to 1 year in advance*

The Memory Garden is a tranquil Spanish-style garden located next to Custom House Plaza. Capacity is approximately five hundred fifty people maximum for a sit-down dinner and two hundred fifty for a stand-up reception. A barbecue pit is available for use with an additional fee. The Memory Garden may be rented for just a wedding ceremony if the ceremony, setup, and teardown are limited to two hours. Reservations may be made through the Monterey State Historic Park up to one year in advance.

Pacific Grove Community Center

515 Junipero Avenue
Pacific Grove, CA 93950
(831) 648-5730

The Community Center in quaint Pacific Grove is available as a rental for single events or for regularly scheduled meetings. This is a wonderful facility for affordable wedding receptions and anniversary parties.

AREA	MAX. CAPACITY	BBQ/ KITCHEN	TABLES	FEE
Lebeck Room	175	BBQ/ kitchen	yes	$350-$75 for 4 hrs

Rest Rooms: *Yes*

Outdoor Night Lighting: *Yes*

Amplified Music: *Yes, with sound permit*

Security Deposit: *$500*

Responsible for Cleanup: *You*

Alcohol Allowed: *Yes*

Permit Required: *Yes*

Insurance Required: *With alcohol*

Gazebo: *No*

Other Amenities: *Dance floor in Lebeck room, outside BBQ, c playground, tennis courts*

Reservations: *As soon as possible or 6 months prior to event d*

PEBBLE BEACH LOCATIONS

Pebble Beach Co. Security Department
17-Mile Drive
Pebble Beach, CA 93953
(831) 625-8427

AREA	MAX. CAPACITY	BBQ/ KITCHEN	TABLES	FEE
Spanish Bay Beach	unlimited	small fires	yes	none
Fanshell Beach	unlimited	small fires	no	none
Lone Cypress	15-20	no	no	none

Rest Rooms: *No*

Outdoor Night Lighting: *No*

Amplified Music: *No*

Security Deposit: *No*

Responsible for Cleanup: *You*

Alcohol Allowed: *Yes*

Permit Required: *No*

Insurance Required: *No*

Gazebo: *No*

Other Amenities: *None*

Reservations: *Apply for permission through Security Department*

Wedding ceremonies are often performed at the breathtaking sites along Pebble Beach's 17-Mile Drive. Spanish Bay Beach and the white sands of Fanshell Beach are both popular spots for larger parties. The famous Lone Cypress, clinging to seemingly bare rock, is also an inspirational spot for a small ceremony. These locations cannot be closed off to tourists, so late-afternoon weddings are recommended.

PFEIFFER BIG SUR STATE PARK

Big Sur Station #1
Big Sur, CA 93920
(831) 667-0158

Pfeiffer Big Sur State Park has three group picnic areas that may be reserved by groups of ten or more. The remaining facilities, including the softball field, may be used on a first-come, first-served basis only.

AREA	MAX. CAPACITY	BBQ/ KITCHEN	TABLES	FEE
Picnic Area #1	100	5 BBQs 1 rock BBQ	yes	$3*
Picnic Area #2	100	4 BBQs	yes	$3*
Picnic Area #3	200	BBQ Pit	yes	$3*

Rest Rooms: *Yes*

Outdoor Night Lighting: *No*

Amplified Music: *No*

Security Deposit: *No*

Responsible for Cleanup: *You*

Alcohol Allowed: *Yes*

Permit Required: *No*

Insurance Required: *No*

Gazebo: *No*

Other Amenities: *Softball field, hiking trails*

Reservations: *Can be made up to 60 days in advance*

Note: ** per vehicle*

PIRATE'S COVE ADVENTURES BY THE SEA

285 Figueroa Street
Monterey, CA 93940
(831) 648-7236

AREA	MAX. CAPACITY	BBQ/ KITCHEN	TABLES	FEE
Picnic Area #1	2,000	yes	yes on deck	yes
Indoor Area	300 sit-down 400 reception	yes	yes	yes

Rest Rooms: *Yes*

Outdoor Night Lighting: *Yes*

Amplified Music: *Yes*

Security Deposit: *Yes*

Responsible for Cleanup: *Adventures by the Sea*

Alcohol Allowed: *Yes*

Permit Required: *Yes*

Insurance Required: *No*

Gazebo: *No*

Other Amenities: *Bike tours, beach Olympics, ocean kayaking, teambuilding programs, company picnics, plus much more*

Reservations: *Can be made up to 1 year in advance*

Adventures by the Sea creates the perfect beach party. This event provides a terrific way to spend a day or evening at the beach relaxing after meetings or simply having fun. Grass huts, palm trees, a roaring bonfire, tiki torches, and volleyball combine with great food and entertainment to create a night to remember. Their beach location includes the Pirate's Cove facility in case of inclement weather. They offer several choices of menus and can combine beach parties with special recreation packages to suit your needs.

TORO COUNTY PARK

501 Monterey/Salinas Highway
Salinas, CA 93908
(831) 484-1108
Reservations: (831) 755-4899

oro County Park is located thirteen miles from the Monterey Peninsula on Highway 68. First opened to the public in 1971, the park's 4,756 acres have been a haven for thousands of visitors. The park is also home to many types of wildlife. There are plenty of activity areas for the sports-minded and over twenty miles of riding and hiking trails. Toro's pastoral setting makes it the ideal site for your next event.

AREA	MAX. CAPACITY	BBQ/ KITCHEN	TABLES	FEE
Oak Grove	150	BBQ pit	yes	$50
Quail Meadow*	500	BBQ pit	yes	$70
Badger Flats	200	BBQ pit	yes	$50
Sycamore	200	BBQ pit	yes	$50
Buckeye*	500	BBQ pit	yes	$70

Rest Rooms: *Yes*

Outdoor Night Lighting: *No*

Amplified Music: *With permit*

Security Deposit: *No*

Responsible for Cleanup: *You*

Alcohol Allowed: *Yes, with permit and in specified areas*

Permit Required: *Yes*

Insurance Required: *Yes, if elements of event require it*

Gazebo: *No*

Other Amenities: *Playgrounds, softball fields, volleyball courts, hiking and riding trails, and horseshoe pits*

Reservations: *Can be made up to 1 year in advance*

*Note: *Does not include vehicle entrance fee*

INTIMATE GATHERINGS DIRECTORY

INTIMATE GATHERINGS DIRECTORY

To help you choose a restaurant for an intimate gathering, we have included the restaurants' cuisine styles and symbols for entrée price ranges. $ means that the entrées are mostly under $14; $$ means that the entrées are mostly under $20; $$$ means that the entrées are mostly under $28.

ANTON & MICHEL

Mission btw. Ocean & 7th
Carmel, CA 93921
(831) 624-2406
CUISINE STYLE: EUROPEAN $$$

At the Court of the Fountains, an enchanting venue in Carmel's "Restaurant of the Year 2000." Elegant hosting of up to 100 guests amid a graciou ambience of soft tones, candlelit decor, an original oil paintings. Unsurpassed servic superb cuisine, and a consistently award-winning wine list exquisitely enhance that special occasion or business gathering

BAJA CANTINA

7166 Carmel Valley Rd.
Carmel, CA 93923
(831) 625-2252
CUISINE STYLE: MEXICAN $

Stop by and fill up with good food and great margaritas at this Carmel Valley roadhouse. Dine on the heated patio overlooking the valley hills or inside surrounded by authentic original auto memorabilia that take you back to the roads, gas stations, and race tracks of the early 1900s. Specialties include grilled and spit roasted meats, fresh seafood, salads, and heavenly enchiladas. Buffet available for large parties. Live entertainment.

CASANOVA

5th St. btw. Mission & San Carlos
Carmel, CA 93921
(831) 625-9799
CUISINE STYLE: COUNTRY.FRENCH $$$

Casanova offers a culinary experience that echoes the south of France and northern Italy in the center of Carmel. The style and ambiance is matched by a standard of excellence in food and service that has brought worldwide acclaim. The hand-dug wine cellar has received numerous awards for its outstanding selection of wines from all over the world.

CIBO

301 Alvarado Street
Monterey, CA 93921
(831) 649-8151
CUISINE STYLE: ITALIAN $$

This simple yet elegant California-style ristorante offers the perfect setting for innovative flavorful interpretations of classic Italian cooking. Salads, pasta, pizza, meat, poultry, and seafood recipes are prepared with fresh, locally grown herbs and vegetables. An impressive selection of fine California and Italian wines is available. Locally voted "Best Italian Restaurant" and "Best Place for Jazz."

CIELO

Ventana Inn & Spa
Highway One
Big Sur, CA 93920
(831) 667-2331
CUISINE STYLE: CALIFORNIA $$$

Cielo, which means "heaven" or "sky" in Spanish, is the restaurant at Ventana Inn & Spa. Situated on 243 acres, 1,200 feet above the rugged Big Sur coastline, the restaurant's warm and rustic interior opens out onto a terrace where panoramic views stretch for fifty miles. An innovative menu offers daily specials made with the best regional ingredients and prepared with robust flavors. Lunch and dinner are served daily.

CLUB JALAPEÑO

San Carlos btw. 5th & 6th
Carmel, CA 93921
(831) 626-1997
CUISINE STYLE: MEXICAN $

A jalapeño is not just a Mexican hot pepper anymore. It's also the name of a popular hot spot in Carmel—Club Jalapeño. You'll find traditional food like enchiladas, tacos, burritos, and tamales, plus specialties like one-of-a-kind chicken rellenos or Club J's famous fish...coconut, banana, or seasoned...an incredible five-spice chicken tostada salad and great vegetarian fare.

THE COVEY

Quail Lodge Resort & Golf Club
8205 Valley Greens Drive
Carmel, CA 93923
(831) 620-8860
CUISINE STYLE: WINE COUNTRY $$$

The Covey Restaurant's Wine Country Cuisine has drawn critical acclaim from the most discerning palates and remains a favorite of local patrons. The freshest products of valley and bay come together in an incredible array of flavors, integrated with textural complexity and layers of varietal character. Enjoy the casual, inviting ambiance of The Covey while overlooking sparkling Mallard Lake.

FANDANGO

223 17th St.
Pacific Grove, CA 93950
(831) 372-3456
CUISINE STYLE: EUROPEAN $$

Enjoy European country-style cuisine in a warm Mediterranean setting. Fandango offers customized menus from freshly prepared regional dishes that are complemented by an extraordinary selection of premium wines and a full-service bar. Private dining rooms include a festive wine cellar and a glass-domed terrace.

THE FISHWIFE AT ASILOMAR

1996 Sunset Dr.
Pacific Grove, CA 93950
(831) 375-7107
CUISINE STYLE: SEAFOOD $

Enjoy award-winning California cuisine with a Caribbean accent, featuring fresh seafood and pasta. Specials from the grill spotlight local fresh catch— halibut, salmon, sand dabs, and snapper. Voted "Best Seafood on the Monterey Peninsula" (1989-2001). The Fishwife serves great food in a friendly atmosphere.

FLAHERTY'S SEAFOOD GRILL & OYSTER BAR

6th btw. San Carlos & Dolores
Carmel, CA 93921
(831) 625-1500
CUISINE STYLE: SEAFOOD $$

Flaherty's offers flexible and attractive plans and facilities for meetings and social gatherings any time of day. Accommodating up to one hundred guests, packages are available from finger food to formal sit-down extravaganzas. Either or both the Oyster Bar and Seafood Grill can be reserved.

Forge in the Forest

Southwest Corner of
5th & Junipero
Carmel, CA 93921
(831) 624-2233
CUISINE STYLE: AMERICAN $$

Discover this 10,000-square-foot historic property in the heart of Carmel. Whether you choose the Wine Cellar, Gallery Room, Oak Tree Room, Oak Tree Patio or a complete property buyout, you will be bathed in ambiance. Combined with the executive chef's custom tailored menus, you are guaranteed an incredible dining experience you and your guests will remember for years to come.

Fresh Cream

100C Heritage Harbor
Monterey, CA 93940
(831) 375-9798
CUISINE STYLE: FRENCH $$$

The Fresh Cream perspective gives a new outlook to those who appreciate fine dining. Stunning views, elegant decor, and impeccable service set the mood for romantic dinners, special evenings, or private dinners for fifteen to one hundred fifty. Classic French cuisine with a California accent is presented with imagination and flair. Winner of the prestigious San Francisco Focus Magazine reader's poll "Best in Monterey County" for seven consecutive years.

The Grill on Ocean Avenue

Ocean Ave. near Lincoln
Carmel, CA 93921
(831) 624-2569
CUISINE STYLE: CALIF.-ASIAN $$

Named one of Monterey's 10 Best Restaurants (Epicurean Rendezvous), offering consistently creative cooking. Cuisine has been described as "lyrical, clearly Californian in its freshness and lightness, clearly Asian in its virtuosity." East meets West with entrees such as Duck Ravioli, Oak-Grilled Salmon, and Pan-Roasted Sea Bass. A relaxed atmosphere, friendly staff, and exceptional California wines round out this "very fresh" dining experience.

Il Fornaio

Monte Verde at Ocean Ave.
Carmel, CA 93921
(831) 622-5100
CUISINE STYLE: ITALIAN $$

Il Fornaio serves award-winning authentic Italian cuisine in Carmel's historic Pine Inn. Their menu includes wood-fired pizza, rotisserie meats and fowl, mesquite-grilled local fish, and fresh regional pastas. Comfortable fireside ocean-view terrace seating. A fifty-seat private dining room is available.

MONTRIO

414 Calle Principal
Monterey, CA 93940
(831) 648-8880
CUISINE STYLE: BISTRO $$

Consistently voted Monterey's "Best Restaurant" in local and regional publications, Montrio is a dynamic location for private parties, meetings, and special events. The bistro-style menus are flexible and designed to fit both occasion and budget. Located in a completely transformed 1910 firehouse, Montrio offers a number of rooms perfect for parties ranging from eight to five hundred.

NICO

San Carlos betw. Ocean & 7th
Carmel, CA 93921
(831) 624-6545
CUISINE STYLE: MEDITERRANEAN $$

Cloaked in sienna-toned walls, with a sky-blue ceiling and an earthstone-gray floor, Nico brings a calming, uplifting presence to the dining experience. The menu features expertly prepared Mediterranean specialties—everything from grilled porcini mushrooms and pepper-seared asparagus to pasta, pizza, seafood, and steak entrées. Nico has mastered the deceptively simple goal of all successful restaurants: serve good food and send people home happy.

THE OAKS

Carmel Valley Ranch
1 Old Ranch Rd.
Carmel Valley, CA 93924
(831) 625-9500
CUISINE STYLE: COASTAL RANCH $$$

Nestled on a forested hillside with glorious valley views, The Oaks dining room is set amidst the countryside charm of a luxurious resort. The menu features Coastal Ranch cuisine with the freshest fruits and vegetables from local farms, fish from coastal waters, and herbs from the resort's own garden. And the wine list has been honored annually by Wine Spectator's "Award for Excellence."

OLD BATH HOUSE RESTAURANT

620 Ocean View Blvd.
Pacific Grove, CA 93950
(831) 375-5195
CUISINE STYLE: NEW AMERICAN $$$

A stunning view of the crashing surf of the Pacific Ocean combined with award-winning cuisine and service to match awaits guests of the Old Bath House Restaurant. Romantic yet sophisticated in style, this is the place to celebrate a special occasion or just enjoy a relaxing evening with friends. The Old Bath House Victorian-era building is within a stones' throw to the beach. A scenic, classic, and romantic location for any event.

PACIFIC'S EDGE

Highlands Inn
Highway One
Carmel, CA 93921
(831) 624-3801
CUISINE STYLE: REGIONAL-CALIF. $$$

The Pacific's Edge offers one of the world's most inspiring ocean vistas—a view matched in magnificence only by the innovative regional California cuisine. Only the freshest seasonal ingredients are used to create dishes that are a feast as much for the eyes as for the palate.

PASSIONFISH

701 Lighthouse Ave.
Pacific Grove, CA 93950
(831) 655-3311
www.passionfish.net
CUISINE STYLE: SEAFOOD $$

Passionfish, located in charming downtown Pacific Grove, features line-caught local fish, slow-cooked meats, and an award-winning wine list priced at retail. Regardless of your group's size, the staff at Passionfish offers easy, flexible menu planning to help customize your special event. Private and semi-private rooms available. No room charges applied.

PENINSULA RESTAURANT

Hyatt Regency
One Old Golf Course Road
Monterey, CA 93940
(831) 647-2033
CUISINE STYLE: AMERICAN $$$

Gather with friends and relax in a warm, inviting atmosphere. Dine and enjoy the view of beautiful manicured gardens while seated on the 17th green of historic Del Monte Golf Course. Peninsula Restaurant features an open kitchen with a state-of-the art eighteen-hundred-degree grill specializing in savory sizzling steaks, seafood, salad, and fresh-baked breads.

PIATTI

6th & Junipero
Carmel, CA 93921
(831) 625-1766
CUISINE STYLE: ITALIAN $$

One of Carmel's favorite gathering places for the past decade, Piatti features Italian regional cuisine from fresh pasta and seafood specials to pizza from the wood burning oven—all served in a cozy, relaxed atmosphere. While dining fireside, savor signature dishes including the house ricotta ravioli in lemon cream, succulent rotisserie chicken, and pancetta-wrapped grilled prawns, complemented by an excellent selection of award-winning wines.

RIO GRILL

Highway One and Rio Rd.
Carmel, CA 93923
(831) 625-5436
CUISINE STYLE: NEW AMERICAN $$

The high energy that is Rio Grill's trademark extends to private parties and business functions. The restaurant's creative California cuisine and consistently outstanding service ensure memorable events. Private parties and meetings are comfortably accommodated in Rio's new Santa Fe room, while several semiprivate areas are also available in the main dining room.

ROBERT'S BISTRO

217 Crossroads Blvd.
Carmel, CA 93923
(831) 624-9626
CUISINE STYLE: FRENCH $$$

A culinary pleasure ground for the senses, Robert's Bistro has been a consistent award winner, from best restaurant to best French restaurant to best chef, and continues to garner critical acclaim. The bistro is set in a rustic European atmosphere with two oversized stone fireplaces. The entire experience, from the respectfully attentive service to the storied cuisine, is designed to produce the same unspoken sense of satisfaction.

THE SARDINE FACTORY

701 Wave St.
Monterey, CA 93940
(831) 373-3775
CUISINE STYLE: SEAFOOD $$$

Luncheon or dinner in the varied venues of the Sardine Factory is offered to groups of up to 100 guests. The Gothic Wine Cellar, the glass-domed Conservatory, or the opulent Captain's Room may be viewed at www.sardinefactory.com. Each event is customized at the Sardine Factory, Monterey's premier award-winning restaurant and the flagship of Cannery Row.

TARPY'S ROADHOUSE

Highway 68 at Canyon Del Rey
Monterey, CA 93940
(831) 647-1444
CUISINE STYLE: NEW AMERICAN $$

With its seven unique dining rooms and two European-style garden patios, this historic stone house is the ideal setting for private parties, weddings, business meetings, and all-day seminars. Tarpy's hearty, country cuisine translates to a variety of menus perfect for any occasion. A superb staff brings it all together for wonderful events that are assured of success.

TERRACE GRILL

La Playa Hotel
8th and Camino Real
Carmel, CA 93921
(831) 624-4010
CUISINE STYLE: NEW AMERICAN $$$

The Terrace Grill, located in the historic La Playa Hotel, has a view of the ocean on one side and immaculate flower gardens on the other. A covered and heated terrace offers alfresco dining at its best! An eclectic contemporary menu includes Almond-Crusted Sole, Artichoke Ravioli, Prime Rib, and the freshest seafood, grilled to perfection.

VILLAGE CORNER

Dolores and 6th Ave.
Carmel, CA 93921
(408) 624-3588
CUISINE STYLE: EUROPEAN $

Welcome to Carmel-by-the-Sea's unique alfresco Mediterranean Bistro. Savor the culinary influences of the Old World and enjoy Spanish paella, Greek and Californian salads, pastas from the sunny isle of Capri, and fresh local seafood. Complement your meal with good wines. Relax on the patio by the fire with a cappuccino and tiramisu, and watch your friends stroll by.

THE TINNERY

631 Ocean View Blvd.
Pacific Grove, CA 93950
(831) 646-1040
CUISINE STYLE: AMERICAN $

The Tinnery boasts unsurpassed views from Lovers Point of the Monterey Bay. Dining is relaxed and affordable, whether your party is in the main dining room, the Cove Room, or Solarium. The Tinnery offers customized menus for large groups or intimate cocktail parties.

VITO'S

1180 Forest Ave.
Pacific Grove, CA 93950
(831) 375-3070
CUISINE STYLE: ITALIAN $$

Voted "Best Italian Restaurant," Vito and his family prepare their recipes with an Old-World flair in a casual and friendly atmosphere. Relax and choose from a menu that includes an extensive array of anitpasti, fresh fish, chicken, veal, pasta entrées and an irresistible dessert menu (including a family-secret tiramisu). In true Sicilian fashion, no one walks away hungry.

CEREMONIES, CHAPELS, CHURCHES, SYNAGOGUES

CEREMONIES

CEREMONIES
CHAPELS
CHURCHES
SYNAGOGUES

Reverend Charles Anker
(831) 625-2382

Reverend Rory Claire
A Beautiful Beginning
(831) 655-8676

Colette Cuccia
Nondenominational Minister
(831) 626-0643

Judge Richard Eldred
Civil Wedding Ceremonies
(831) 372-7754

John Kelly
Nondenominational Minister
(831) 375-5540

Reverend Brian Lyke
Life Celebrations
(831) 625-6535

Dr. Charles Murillo
Nondenominational Minister
831-626-7003

Patt O'Brien
A By-the-Sea Wedding
(831) 649-1819

Reverend Robert Tarr
(831) 659-4675

Chapels/Churches

All Saint's Episcopal Church
9th and Dolores (P.O. Box 1296)
Carmel, CA 93921
(831) 624-3883

Bethlehem Lutheran Church of
Monterey
800 Cass St.
Monterey, CA 93940
(831) 373-1523

Calvary Chapel Monterey Bay
3001 Monterey-Salinas Hwy.
Monterey, CA 93940
(831) 649-1158

Carmel Mission Basilica
Rio Rd. and Lasuen Dr. (P.O. Box 2235)
Carmel, CA 93921
(831) 624-1271

Carmel Presbyterian Church
Ocean and Junipero (P.O. Box 846)
Carmel, CA 93921
(831) 624-3878

Central Presbyterian Church of
Monterey—Korean
325 Central Ave.
Pacific Grove, CA 93950
(831) 375-7207

Christian Church Disciples of Christ of
Pacific Grove
Carmel Ave. and Central Ave.
Pacific Grove, CA 93950
(831) 372-0363

Church in the Forest
Forest Lake Rd.
Pebble Beach, CA 93953
(831) 624-1374

Church of Christ
(Nondenominational)
176 Central Ave.
Pacific Grove, CA 93950
(831) 375-3741

Church of the Wayfarer
Lincoln and 7th Ave.
Carmel, CA 93921
(831) 624-3550

Community Church of the Monterey
Peninsula
(Nondenominational)
Carmel Valley Rd.
Carmel, CA 93923
(831) 624-8595

First Baptist Church
(Conservative)
600 Hawthorne St.
Monterey, CA 93940
(831) 373-3289

First Baptist Church of Carmel Valley
8340 Carmel Valley Rd.
Carmel Valley, CA 93924
(831) 624-5551

First Church of God
(Nondenominational)
1023 David Ave.
Pacific Grove, CA 93950
(831) 372-5005

First United Methodist Church of
Pacific Grove
Sunset Dr. and 17-Mile Dr.
Pacific Grove, CA 93950
(831) 372-5875

Immaculate Heart Hermitage
New Camaldoli
Route One
Big Sur, CA 93920
(831) 667-2456

Islamic Society of Monterey County
(831) 644-8332

Korean Buddhist Temple Sambosa
28110 Robinson Canyon Rd.
Carmel, CA 93923
(831) 624-3686

Living Hope Church of the Nazarene
Highway 68 and Josselyn Canyon Rd.
Monterey, CA 93940
(831) 375-4414

Mayflower Presbyterian Church
Central Ave. and 14th St.
Pacific Grove, CA 93950
(831) 373-4705

Monterey Assembly of God
317 Virgin Ave.
Monterey, CA 93940
(831) 655-2500

Monterey Stone Marriage Chapel
2999 Monterey-Salinas Hwy.
Monterey, CA 93940
(831)375-1900

Our Lady of Mt. Carmel Church
El Caminito Rd.
Carmel Valley, CA 93924
(831) 659-2224

Pacific Grove Congregation of
Jehovah's Witnesses
1100 Sunset Dr.
Pacific Grove, CA 93950
(831) 375-2138

Peninsula Christian Center
520 Pine Ave.
Pacific Grove, CA 93950
(831) 373-0431

Peninsula Presbyterian Church
702 Forest Ave.
Pacific Grove, CA 93950
(831) 375-5510

St. Angela's Catholic Church
146 8th St.
Pacific Grove, CA 93950
(831) 655-4160

St. Mary's By-the-Sea Episcopal Church
Central Ave. and 12th St.
Pacific Grove, CA 93950
(831) 373-4441

St. Philip's Lutheran Church
8065 Carmel Valley Rd.
Carmel, CA 93923
(831) 624-6765

San Carlos Cathedral
550 Church St.
Monterey, CA 93940
(831) 373-2628

Seventh-Day Adventist Church of the
Monterey Peninsula
375 Lighthouse Ave.
Pacific Grove, CA 93950
(831) 372-7818

Unitarian Universalist Church of the
Monterey Peninsula
490 Aguajito Rd.
Carmel, CA 93923
(831) 624-4704

Unity Church of Monterey
601 Madison
Monterey, CA 93940
(831) 372-0457

SYNAGOGUES
Congregation Beth Israel
5716 Carmel Valley Rd.
Carmel, CA 93923
(831) 624-2015

Temple Beth El
1212 Riker
Salinas, CA
(831) 424-9151

LOCAL RESOURCES TO HELP YOU PLAN

A
BIRD OF
PARADISE

Event IS UNIQUE

OUR FOOD   *has bold, fresh, bright flavors with splashy colors, fresh herbs, and flavors. The freshest product. . . not only artfully arranged, it tastes fantastic!*

CHEF JON KASKY   *was influenced by his experience with Wolfgang Puck, Jeremiah Towers, Alice Waters & Ken Hom at the California Culinary Academy. Upon graduating with honors, he became the private chef at a major California winery, where he remained until founding BIRD OF PARADISE in 1985.*

MENU   *-Be prepared to play a real part in creating your wedding menu: we don't sell "canned" menus. Chef Jon takes the time to meet with you and discover your needs; out of this interaction evolves a personalized menu that reflects your style and taste.*

USE BIRD OF PARADISE WHEN FOOD MATTERS. CALL AND MAKE AN APPOINTMENT TO MEET US.
(831) 659-3417

Paradise
CATERING
www.paradisecater.com

- Weddings & Rehearsal Dinners

- Private Intimate Dinners

- Sit Down Buffets

- Breakfast, & Lunch

- Receptions

- Corporate Events

- Bar / Bat Mitzvah

- Barbeques

- Beach Parties

- Event Planning & Services

MICHAEL'S
CATERING

Full Service Catering
Since 1983

800 773-5232

A BY-THE-SEA WEDDING
and
MONTEREY STONE CHAPEL

A COMPLETE WEDDING SERVICE

Beautiful Ocean Settings, Romantic Monterey
Stone Chapel or a location of your choice
Full receptions & dinners available on-site
at Tarpy's Roadhouse Restaurant

License Issued • Photos, Video & Flowers Available

REV. PATT O'BRIEN (831) 375-8574
www.montereyweddings.com

NOTES

Index

ABOUT THE AUTHOR

Janice Block, author of *Locations, Locations, Locations,* has made her home on the Monterey Peninsula for more than 25 years. Over the past 25 years, she has been involved with every aspect of the hospitality business. In addition to authoring *Locations, Locations, Locations,* Janice is co-publisher of *Critic's Choice Recipe Collection: 145 Recipes from the Monterey Peninsula's Best Restaurants* and *The Dining Guide,* which is going into its 16th year of circulation with more than two million copies in print.

Janice has worked as a special-event location consultant since 1986 and has helped countless brides and meeting planners find the ideal setting for their event. A world traveler, Pilates enthusiast, and avid tennis player, Janice also has a California real-estate license.

THE BEACH RESORT

DETAILS ON PAGE 46

CASANOVA RESTAURANT

DETAILS ON PAGE 14

FANDANGO

DETAILS ON PAGE 16

THE FORGE IN THE FOREST

DETAILS ON PAGE 18

FRESH CREAM

DETAILS ON PAGE 20

HIGHLANDS INN

DETAILS ON PAGE 58

THE HOLLY FARM

DETAILS ON PAGE 112

LA PLAYA HOTEL

DETAILS ON PAGE 66

MARTINE INN

DETAILS ON PAGE 72

MISSION RANCH

DETAILS ON PAGE 74

MONTREY MARRIOTT

DETAILS ON PAGE 78

MONTEREY PLAZA

DETAILS ON PAGE 80

PASSIONFISH

DETAILS ON PAGE 28

QUAIL LODGE & RESORT

DETAILS ON PAGE 82

SARDINE FACTORY

DETAILS ON PAGE 32

STOKES RESTAURANT & BAR
DETAILS ON PAGE 34

TARPY'S ROADHOUSE RESTAURANT

DETAILS ON PAGE 36

VENTANA INN & SPA

DETAILS ON PAGE 86